Three Persons, One God

Growing in relationship with the
Father, Son, and Holy Spirit

A Faith Sharing Guide

Three Persons, One God

Growing in relationship with the Father, Son, and Holy Spirit

Allison Gingras

LEONINE PUBLISHERS
PHOENIX, ARIZONA

The Scripture citations used in this work, unless otherwise indicated, are taken from the *New American Bible: Revised Edition*, copyright © 2011 by Oxford University Press, Inc.

Published by Leonine Publishers LLC
PO Box 8099
Phoenix, Ariz. 85066

ISBN-13: 978-0-9859483-8-2

10 9 8 7 6 5 4 3 2 1

Printed in the United States of America

Library of Congress Control Number: 2012949661

Visit us online at www.leoninepublishers.com
For more information: info@leoninepublishers.com

Dedication

I wish to dedicate this book to:

My amazing husband, Kevin Gingras, truly chosen by God to be my partner on this earthly journey. Thanks for always holding down the fort while I chase my dream of working for God's Kingdom.

Julie Frank—a gift from God to be a wonderful friend and talented, encouraging editor.

The Bible ladies who poured over the first drafts with me:

Ana Burke

Marianne DiCorpo

Cindy Darrer

Mary Jo Foley

Heather Kirby

Paula Lauzon

Darlene McAuley

Vicki Serra

Karen Toste

Tammy Woodford

My beautiful children—Ian, Adam, and Faith.

And my sister, Kristen Perry, who got the ball rolling on my first try at this many years ago.

Contents

Introduction

Parable of the Farmer Scattering Seed

⁴One day Jesus told a story in the form of a parable to a large crowd that had gathered from many towns to hear him: ⁵"A farmer went out to plant his seed. As he scattered it across his field, some seed fell on a footpath, where it was stepped on, and the birds ate it. ⁶Other seed fell among rocks. It began to grow, but the plant soon wilted and died for lack of moisture. ⁷Other seed fell among thorns that grew up with it and choked out the tender plants. ⁸Still other seed fell on fertile soil. This seed grew and produced a crop that was a hundred times as much as had been planted!" When he had said this, he called out, "Anyone with ears to hear should listen and understand."

⁹His disciples asked him what this parable meant. ¹⁰He replied, "You are permitted to understand the secrets of the Kingdom of God. But I use parables to teach the others so that the Scriptures might be fulfilled:

'When they look, they won't really see.
When they hear, they won't understand.'

¹¹"This is the meaning of the parable: The seed is God's word. ¹²The seeds that fell on the footpath represent those who hear the message, only to have the devil come and take it away from their hearts and prevent them from believing and being saved. ¹³The seeds on the rocky soil represent

those who hear the message and receive it with joy. But since they don't have deep roots, they believe for a while then they fall away when they face temptation. [14]The seeds that fell among the thorns represent those who hear the message, but all too quickly the message is crowded out by the cares and riches and pleasures of this life. And so they never grow into maturity. [15]And the seeds that fell on the good soil represent honest, good-hearted people who hear God's word, cling to it, and patiently produce a huge harvest.[1]

Perhaps it is with age that I can now look at this parable in relation to my own faith journey. When I was a child, my parents would bring me to Mass where I would hear three readings and a responsorial psalm. Sadly, I have to admit, I was in my mid-thirties before I had any idea it was the Bible I was hearing. This fact eluded me throughout my entire religious education. Either it was never taught, or certainly not mentioned often enough for it to become part of my faith knowledge. Somewhere I missed the crucial point that these words are the life-giving Word of God. Just like the seeds on the rocky path in the parable, I heard the Word, but the devil took full advantage of my ignorance, and snatched the meaning away before it could penetrate my heart.

As time passed, I made attempts to grow in my faith by attending different retreat programs. There, I was re-awakened to the things of God. Suddenly, Mass had a new energy, the readings had a new place for me as God breathed, and the homilies touched my heart, as if they were written just for me. Filled with a new desire to become closer to God, I vowed to say a daily rosary, attend Mass faithfully, and not avoid my yearly required confession. For a bit, I'd sing a little louder in church, long for my prayer time, and even subscribe to a Catholic magazine. Yet, over time, without the encouraging support of the retreat team, the consistent study of Scripture or finding quiet time for prayer—all wonderful ways to nourish a tender sprout of faith—the roots were not strengthened and it withered away again. However, this left behind an empty feeling within me; a thirst for

---

[1] Luke 8:4-15 (New Living Translation)

something more, perhaps even a longing for those euphoric feelings experienced during the days, weeks, and even months following the retreats.

As I grew older, my focus became being a wife, mother (occasional nurse, counselor, teacher), homemaker (cook, housekeeper, chauffer), as well as a plethora of assorted careers. The thorns of this world grew all around me. Any seeds dropped by priests, friends, or the occasional inspirational speaker would be choked with the weeds of daily worries, concerns, and tasks.

Time spent with any "religious" reading materials—books, magazines, the Bible—would cease to exist. I hardly had enough time to read bedtime stories to my children, never mind the Bible, which I struggled to understand anyway. Prayer would consist of a quick blessing before meals (if the family was enjoying a rare meal together), or the obligatory Our Father or Hail Mary before drifting off to sleep. This was a habit I probably continued to practice only because my grandmother taught it to me as a child, and had become ingrained as a normal part of bedtime routine, more than a conscious effort to review my conscience or spend quality time with the Lord.

The one thing that did remain consistent was my weekly attendance at Mass, but not because I felt spiritual growth from it. It was my insurance policy. I imagined that God put a check mark next to my name on some heavenly attendance sheet so I could be sure to be remembered at the hour of my death. At least, that is how I saw it during the spare moments I would give any thought to "things of above," in between my kid's music lessons, soccer games, and other activities, not to mention my board meetings, school volunteering, and social engagements. The thorns of this world were choking the tender plants, providing me little opportunity to grow in my faith.

So how do we achieve planting ourselves in good soil? For some, this cultivation is ushered in by a life-altering event. Perhaps a tragedy or trial awakens a desire to seek something beyond what this world has to offer. Possibly it is in experiencing firsthand that this life is fleeting and our paths are paved with so much suffering that our innate yearning for the Lord emerges. For others, it is a lull in life as their children grow and become more independent, or actually leave the nest. Finally able to take time for their own pursuits, they join a group at the church, or a Bible study and their journey of learning about God and His promises begins anew. The catalysts are as varied as the people whom God created, but the one commonality is a desire for a relationship, the desire to "draw near to God, and He will draw near to you."[2]

The soil is tilled and ready, but in order for this seed to really grow, additional effort is required. Weeds must be pulled so we can clearly see where we are drawn to, or away from, the Lord. Fertilizing the soil is critical—through reading and contemplation of the Scriptures or the daily Mass readings. Our faith is watered by increased prayer. In addition, our faith needs nurturing, which we can do by participation in the Sacraments. Sacraments are grace-filled, life-giving, and absolutely essential to the well-being of healthy spiritual gardens.

I pray your soil will be well-nourished by this faith sharing, and nurtured not only by you, but also by the fellow gardeners with whom you share this time. May your faith grow deep roots and flourish in the warmth of the Son.

~ *Allison Gingras*

---

[2] James 4:8

Chapter 1

Discovering God: The Father

For all who are being led by the Spirit of God, these are sons of God.

For you have not received a spirit of slavery leading to fear again, but you have received a spirit of adoption as sons by which we cry out,

"Abba! Father!"

The Spirit Himself testifies with our spirit that we are children of God, and if children, heirs also, heirs of God and fellow heirs with Christ, if indeed we suffer with Him so that we may also be glorified with Him.

Romans 8:14-17

God, the Father

The word "father" brings up many different images. If you come from a household where Dad was home by dinner every night, involved in your extracurricular activities, and tucked you into bed, the characteristics you associate with father may include "loving," "attentive," and "faithful." If, however, you were raised in a household where Dad was busy with his own projects or career, perhaps was an alcoholic or had a temper, then "father" to you is distant, harsh or punitive.

It can be extremely difficult, and take considerable effort, for some to see the Heavenly Father for who He truly is, without imposing on Him our own image of the fathers we have encountered here on Earth. Whether intentional or not, the way we perceive God as Father may not be based on truth as much as on associations we make or experiences we've had. The journey to discover who God the Father really is can be started in Scripture, where God through Divine Revelation begins to reveal himself to us.

Since Scripture is divinely inspired by God, the Bible can be considered somewhat autobiographical. We can catch glimpses of who God really is, just as Moses in the cleft of the rock[1] experienced a burst of His glory. In these amazing revelatory moments, we grow closer to God, the real God, and therefore discard the skewed impression of Him we have unconsciously developed.

> God is the *Father* Almighty, whose fatherhood and power shed light on one another: God reveals his fatherly omnipotence by the way he takes care of our needs; by the filial adoption that he gives us ("I will be a father to you, and you shall be my sons and daughters, says the Lord Almighty"): finally by his infinite mercy, for he displays his power at its height by freely forgiving sins.
>
> *Catechism of Catholic Church (CCC), 270 (emphasis in original)*

---

[1] Exodus 33:18-23

The Character of God

Consider your image of God and how you relate to God as Father. What ideas have you formed about God and His role in your life? Where do you think those beliefs have come from?

Scripture Search

There are certain truths about God which Scripture reveals to us. As God is unchanging, we can rely on these characteristics to be steadfast and true. Record how God is characterized in each of the following verses.

Deuteronomy 7:9

Isaiah 41:10

John 14:7

Hebrews 6:17

James 1:17

The first obstacle for some in creating a real, authentic, close relationship with God, is seeing Him as loving, kind, and merciful, and understanding that He desires to be personally connected to you. He desires to have with you a relationship of two-way communication, founded upon trust and love. This will take time to develop, but it is possible. You must start by learning who God really is.

We know of God through Divine Revelation, in Sacred Scripture and through Sacred Tradition. God will not hide from us. He wants to make Himself known and our souls want to know him. As St. Augustine wrote, "my soul is restless, until it rests in You, O Lord." We find God in the Sacraments, in our prayers, in the world around us and in the Holy Bible.

In this book, we will focus primarily on Scripture, where we can read, learn, and begin to develop a better awareness of how to recognize God's voice. Saint Jerome said that "being ignorant of scripture is being ignorant of Jesus." That is true of the entire Trinity—we cannot be afraid to open God's Word and discover the treasures of our Faith that lie within the pages.

The vastness of God cannot be contained in a book. However, there is a plethora of valuable insights we can gain from delving into the Bible. Contemplate all you have learned about God in just five short verses—His faithfulness, loyalty, strength, protection, unchanging nature, and generosity. He is a promise keeper. And you discovered the reflective quality of Jesus on the Father. We've only skimmed the surface. James 4:8 teaches us, "draw near to God, and He will draw near to you."

Journaling

In light of the verses we studied, are your perceptions of God changing? If not, have you learned anything new about Him? What would you like God to reveal to you? How can Sacred Scripture help you learn more about God, or get to know God better? Take time to ponder these questions, and any others burning in your heart. Journal your thoughts below.

Through the Scripture verses in this chapter we've seen that God is unchanging, faithful, steadfast, loving, and that He keeps his promises to us. Unfortunately society is filled with broken promises, overworked and absentee fathers, and expectations that skew our perceptions. If that doesn't veil the truth about God enough, we are also taught that we should "fear God." We are told stories from the Old Testament of the wrath of God, causing us to create the wrong type of fear of the Lord. Instead of a reverent "fear" which means to be in awe, we see Him as ever ready to severely punish us for the first mistake we make. It is no wonder the concept of building a loving relationship seems so foreign.

Even as a young adult, I believed that God was watching me from Heaven, waiting for me to mess up so He could "smite" me, and condemn me to Hell. I never thought of Him as loving, gentle, kind, and protective. I shied away from prayer, afraid to talk to Him, thereby robbing myself of growth in faith and growth in my knowledge of God. In addition, I kept waiting for these "magical moments" when I'd be overcome with grandiose feelings for God. How could I have expected this with a complete stranger? It is important for us to see God as trustworthy in order to allow Him into our hearts and foster an authentic relationship. It requires time and attention to develop a trusting relationship; a parent/child bond—much as what happens with a child and his or her adoptive parent.

I am an adoptive mother and I am a biological mother. While waiting to travel to China to bring home my daughter, I often wondered about the type of relationship she and I would share. I have to admit, there were moments when I worried I would not be able to love her the same way I loved my biological children. Those fears melted completely away as I held that beautiful child in my arms and looked into her eyes. I did indeed love her in the exact same unconditional way as I did the children God had brought into my life through my body. I was her mother, same as theirs, without question.

This realization held more of a miracle than just validating our attaching and bonding. This experience revealed a much greater truth to my heart. As I thought of my relationship with God, especially in the person of my Heavenly Father, I always wondered if He was able to love me in the same way He loves Jesus. As God's adopted child, I was convinced of the impossibility of His feeling about me as He does for Jesus, even before you factor in Jesus' perfect nature verses my sinful one! But, as I looked at my daughter and then at my sons, now knowing the gift of parenthood through both adoption and birth, I knew, without a shadow of a doubt, that God loves me as He does Jesus. It is a different love because I am a creature, and Jesus is the Word of God, but God the Father loves me infinitely as I am! God is Jesus' Father. God is my Father. Without question.

Chapter 2

Recognizing God: The Son

⁵Have this attitude in yourselves which was also in Christ Jesus, ⁶who, although He existed in the form of God, did not regard equality with God a thing to be grasped, ⁷but emptied Himself, taking the form of a bond-servant, and being made in the likeness of men. ⁸Being found in appearance as a man, He humbled Himself by becoming obedient to the point of death, even death on a cross. ⁹For this reason also, God highly exalted Him, and bestowed on Him the name which is above every name ¹⁰so that at the name of Jesus every knee will bow, of those who are in heaven and on earth and under the earth, ¹¹and that every tongue will confess that Jesus Christ is Lord, to the glory of God the Father.

Philippians 2:5-11

God, the Son

In this chapter, we are going to focus not on the divinity of Jesus Christ, but on His humanity. It is all too easy to minimize Jesus' suffering and death by thinking His divinity outweighed or overshadowed the fact that He is fully human. We know from the writing of John[2] that Jesus was with the Father in Heaven from the beginning. Genesis also alludes to this in the use of the plural in the creation of humankind being, "made in **our** image."[3] These passages may cause some to think that if this god-man already had a taste of Heaven, He could easily endure whatever suffering He must in order to return. Thinking of Jesus as more divine than human can truly rob the believer of a deeper understanding of the sacrifice of Jesus Christ. One may truly wonder at what God, in the person of Jesus, did for each one of us.

God allowed Himself to be born of woman, as an infant—fully dependent on man for all His needs. He lived a very humble and meager existence, a laborer and simple Man. Since there is really no detailed record of what Jesus' childhood, adolescence, and young adulthood was like, many surmise that it was a very ordinary life. We can make a rather comfortable assumption that He was educated by His parents, learned His Jewish faith, did chores, and apprenticed under Joseph as a carpenter. The Gospel of Luke provides a possible clue of who He was at age twelve when He is found teaching in the temple.[4] After being found by an anxious Mary and Joseph, we are told that He "went down with them to Nazareth,"[5] and, "increased in wisdom and in years, and in divine and human favor."[6] We can only wonder at the revelations God the Father was allowing Jesus to experience in His humanity as they awaited the appointed day for His public ministry to begin.

---

[2] John 1:1-3

[3] Genesis 1:26

[4] Luke 2:41-52

[5] Luke 2:48

[6] Luke 2:52

How easy it is for us, as Easter people, to skip over the characteristic of Jesus' humanity—especially as son of both God and Mary. Jesus is the ultimate model of Christian behavior. We would do well to look more closely at the "duality" of Jesus portrayed in Scripture in order to better understand and grow closer to Him, and to grow in our own holiness.

> During the greater part of his life Jesus shared the condition of the vast majority of human beings: a daily life spent without evident greatness, a life of manual labor. His religious life was that of a Jew obedient to the law of God, a life in the community. From this whole period it is revealed to us that Jesus was "obedient" to his parents and that he "increased in wisdom and in stature, and in favor with God and man."
>
> *CCC, 531*

The Character of Jesus

Take a few minutes to consider who Jesus is to you. How do you relate to Jesus as the Son? Do you relate more to the divine or the human nature of Jesus? What ideas have you formed about Jesus and His role in your life?

_____

_____

_____

_____

_____

_____

_____

_____

_____

_____

_____

_____

_____

_____

Scripture Search

Let's take a look at some examples of Jesus' human nature. What deeper revelation of the character of Jesus can we surmise from these verses?

Matthew 21:12-13

_____

_____

Mark 14:32-36

_____

_____

Luke 8:45-48

_____

_____

John 11:35

_____

_____

John 19:26-27

_____

_____

How many beautiful examples of Jesus' humanity can we discover throughout Sacred Scripture? We see His anger in the temple. Remember anger in of itself is not a sin, but how we respond to the feeling of anger can be. Jesus' anger shows us great zeal for His Father's house, for what is sacred, right, and just. We cannot become self-righteous or hard-hearted, but must defend our Faith and Church, in love and truth, especially when we know something is harmful or unjust.

The story of the hemorrhaging woman[7] provides such a beautiful insight into the heart of Jesus. Remember, being touched by an unclean woman would have caused Jesus to be deemed unclean according to the Jewish laws of the time. How many times have we encountered the homeless, infirm, or unclean and instead of being compassionate, we recoil? Yet, Jesus stops and seeks her out, touched by her courage and strength. He doesn't see her as dirty, but sees into her heart, as His Father does. He is touched, or moved, by her faith, and it is that faith which He proclaims has healed her. This verse demonstrates so beautifully the gentle, loving, and kind qualities inherent in Jesus' humanity.

Let us look at the poignant scene among Jesus, the Apostle John, and Our Blessed Mother Mary, on Calvary. Jesus at the completion of his earthly ministry turns to the beloved disciple and presents Mary to John as his own mother. Jesus then turns to Mary, in the same way presents John as her own son. Although necessary for Mary's physical well-being and care at that time, Jesus is thinking of far more than simply His Mother and John. Jesus is concerned for all of us—more than 2,000 years' worth of souls yet to be created. The gift he gives at this moment from the Cross, with the simple words "Son, behold your Mother; Mother, behold your Son,"[8] is so profound. Jesus bestows upon each of us the care of His Blessed Mother, to be our mother and a great intercessor and lover of our soul—fulfilling both the work of His humanity and divinity.

---

[7] Luke 8:45
[8] John 19:26-27

Journaling

Scripture tells us that when Mary finds the twelve year-old Jesus in the temple, He states that he must be about His Father's work. Jesus, however, is obedient to His earthly parents and returns home with them. Once there, we are told that she "pondered these things in her heart." Perhaps one of the things she pondered was the affirmation of her son's divinity, and if she will ever fully understand this in her own heart. Take some time to ponder how you see Jesus as the Son of God and as the Son of Man.

_____

_____

_____

_____

_____

_____

_____

_____

_____

_____

_____

_____

To continue to foster a closer relationship with God, we need to encounter Him as the Son, in the person of Jesus Christ. Jesus, our ultimate model of Christian life and the personification of God, can provide us with much insight into knowing God better and growing closer to Him. It is important to relate to Jesus' humanity so we can see our own ability to lead a holy life and therefore be pleasing to God. As we practice relating to Jesus the human Person, we can learn and remember that Jesus was like us in all things, except sin.[9]

This means that Jesus had the same free will we have, and that He could have chosen a less painful path, but chose obedience. How many times have we, when faced with choices, been willing to accept that which would please God, even if it meant not obtaining what we would like? Jesus shows us in the Garden of Gethsemane just how difficult that choice can be. Jesus' agony over this decision was so profound that His sweat became drops of blood. Yet, as He prayed for the strength to choose the Father's will over His own, He provides us an invaluable example of bringing all things to our Heavenly Father through prayer. Choose any Gospel and follow Jesus through it. Note how many times He steals away from His disciples and family to be alone with God and pray. It is a great lesson; it's an example given for us to follow, for we see that it was Jesus' prayer and often fasting that empowered Him to endure the temptations of Satan in the desert and not fall into sin.

Here's something to consider. Are we not in that desert every day? We are tempted by the enemy every day. The choices we make, like Jesus', must be grounded in prayer and when necessary, fasting as well.

Where can we steal away to be with God? That will be different for each of us. But, something that is available to all of us is Eucharistic Adoration. Nearly every Catholic Church provides some time during the month for Exposition of the Blessed Sacrament. Furthermore, most dioceses in the United States have at least one location where twenty-four hour Perpetual Adoration is offered.

---

[9] *CCC*, 470

Let me offer an analogy between the difference of praying at home and making the time to go to adoration. I think most of us can relate to this analogy because we've all had a grandparent or parent with whom we wish we could visit more often.

It is wonderful when we think of Grandma. It is nice to have her in our thoughts and remember times spent with her or conversations we have shared. Sometimes we actually find time to pick up a phone and call Grandma. She loves to hear our voice, and we always hang up smiling at her quirky ways or funny stories. It feels good to make time to converse with Grandma. Yet it is not the same as being with her face-to-face.

However, the times are precious when we are able to put aside our activities and errands, take time away from school or work, close our computers, curb our social engagements, and drive over to see Grandma. Imagine how important she feels when you've made her a priority for that day, especially if it is not Christmas or Easter. You said to her by your mere presence, "You are important to me." Your physical presence illustrates to her that she means something to you; your relationship is valuable to you and that you want to nurture it. The same can be said of our carving out time to visit Jesus in the Blessed Sacrament. Taking the time and effort to visit Our Lord in Eucharistic Adoration affords us the quiet opportunity to ponder His humanity and divinity and, therefore, grow closer to Him.

Chapter 3

Knowing God: The Holy Spirit

[5]and hope does not disappoint, because the love of God has been poured out within our hearts through the Holy Spirit who was given to us.

Romans 5:5

God, the Holy Spirit

How much do you know about the work of the Holy Spirit? It is God's Holy Spirit, the one sent down from Heaven on Pentecost after Jesus ascended. The Holy Spirit bestows seven gifts: wisdom, understanding, counsel, fortitude, knowledge, piety, and fear of the Lord. Catholics believe they are sealed with the Holy Spirit in Confirmation, a completion of their Baptism. This is just more evidence of how, "every good and perfect gift comes from above."[10] However, do you see this gift-giver as a Person, someone you can know and grow close to, or just a favor grantor?

In addition, our cooperation with and our living in the Holy Spirit bears spiritual fruit in us. According to the tradition of the Catholic Church there are twelve fruits of the Spirit: "love, joy, peace, patience, kindness, goodness, faithfulness, gentleness, self-control."[11] If there is an absence of any of these virtues in our lives, this is an area where we can pray and invite the Holy Spirit in.

Still this is not all the Holy Spirit does! He confers the graces received in the Seven Sacraments. Grace can be thought of as that freely given, yet underserved gift from God, which helps us to be holy. God asks us to be holy because He is holy.[12] This Sacramental grace transforms us, heals us, and allows us to grow in faith.

> The Holy Spirit is "the principle of every vital and truly saving action in each part of the Body." He works in many ways to build up the whole Body in charity: by God's Word "which is able to build you up"; by Baptism, through which he forms Christ's Body; by the sacraments, which give growth and healing to Christ's members; by "the grace of the apostles, which holds first place among his gifts"; by the virtues, which make us act according to what is good; finally, by the many special graces (called "charisms"), by which he makes the faithful "fit and ready to undertake various tasks and offices for the renewal and building up of the Church" (*CCC*, 798).

[10] James 1:17

[11] Galatians 5:22-23; *CCC*, 1832

[12] Leviticus 11:44; Matthew 5:48

The Character of the Holy Spirit

Contemplate the characteristics of the Holy Spirit as you understand them to be. How do you see the Holy Spirit manifested in your life? When you pray—do you focus your prayers to the Father, Son, or Holy Spirit? Why do you believe that is?

_____

_____

_____

_____

_____

_____

_____

_____

_____

_____

_____

_____

_____

Scripture Search

The Catechism of the Catholic Church lists eight symbols of the Holy Spirit—Water, Anointing, Fire, Cloud and Light, Sealed Hand, Finger, and Dove.[13] Examine the following verses. Can you identify the Holy Spirit's outward appearance? Can you recognize the Spirit's presence in your own life?

John 4:10-14

2 Corinthians 1:21-22

Acts 2:3-4

Luke 9:34-35

---

[13] *CCC,* 694–701

Ephesians 1:13

Acts 8:17

Exodus 31:18

Genesis 8:8-12

The Holy Spirit appears in many forms as illuminated in the teaching of the *Catechism of the Catholic Church*. Although considered unseen, the Holy Spirit once manifested in these symbols can be perceived. One symbol is water, especially present at the sacrament of Baptism. The Spirit is also present in the living water, Christ, the source of eternal life. At the well, Jesus told the woman that whoever drank of this water would never thirst again. The Spirit brings hope and a promise of eternal life.[14]

Probably the most familiar symbol of the Holy Spirit is that of fire, which came as tongues above the Apostles heads during

---

[14] John 4:14

Pentecost. With this fire came great gifts of prophecy, healing, discernment, and tongues, among others. Fire can also be an agent of refinement, a transformation of the original to a new, more purified form—as with gold.[15] This infusion of the Holy Spirit within us, purifying and shaping us, brings with it new life and understanding of the gifts God grants us. We are each given our own gifts, so that we may play an important, yet unique role in His good and perfect plan for us. The Holy Spirit, the Paraclete, guides and directs us, empowers and motivates us, dwelling within, branded upon our souls as we experience our own daily Pentecost.

As with the Apostles at the original Pentecost, we are commissioned to go out and spread the Good News. With this responsibility comes a blessing, or an anointing. We are told in the Catechism[16] that *Messiah* means the one anointed by God's Spirit, and that another symbol of the Spirit is in anointing. It is this very Spirit that brings about the incarnation of Jesus, placing Him in the womb of Mary and then later the same Spirit that raises him from the dead. We, too, are filled or anointed by this Spirit, especially those who have received the sacrament of Confirmation. At Confirmation, we are anointed with the Chrism Oil, which is a sign that we are being strengthened by and sealed with the Holy Spirit. The sacraments of Baptism and Confirmation, as well as Holy Orders, seal us as children of God. The Spirit imprints on our souls a mark that no force in the universe can destroy; we are forever imbedded with God's imprint of ownership on our hearts.

We cannot consider the symbols of a dove as well as of cloud and light, without also viewing the two instances in the Bible when the Trinity is present together. The first is at Jesus' Baptism; the second, at the Transfiguration. On the first occasion, the Baptism of the Lord, we see the Spirit as a dove. Later, on the mountaintop during His Transfiguration, Peter, James, and John are able to see Jesus as His

---

[15] 1 Peter 1:7

[16] *CCC,* 695

glorified self. In both instances, we hear God, the Father, say, "This is my Son, the Beloved; with him I am well pleased; listen to him."[17]

While clearly present in the form of a dove at the Baptism, it is easy to overlook the Spirit's presence at the Transfiguration unless you are aware of the symbol of cloud and light. The voice of God came in a cloud that overshadowed the three Apostles on hand to witness this magnificent sight. Each time the light reveals what the cloud conceals—the Spirit in this form is illuminating the saving God.[18]

Lastly, the Holy Spirit is represented by fingers and hands. Although there is much about Monty Python that is not godly, their depiction of a giant hand with pointed finger coming from a cloud does have some merit. And perhaps Michelangelo recognized this when he painted the finger of God on the ceiling of the Sistine Chapel. We believe God is infinitely greater than just a finger in a cloud, but it was the finger of God which etched the Commandments upon the tablets that Moses held. We see the hands of God at work through the Apostles, especially in bringing healing. As they laid hands upon people to heal them, it wasn't by their power, but by God's. It was God's Holy Spirit filling the people, and His hand upon them that brought healing—both spiritually and in some cases, physically. "But we all, with unveiled face, beholding as in a mirror the glory of the Lord, are being transformed into the same image from glory to glory, just as from the Lord, the Spirit."[19]

---

[17] Matthew 17:5
[18] *CCC*, 697
[19] 2 Corinthians 3:18

Journaling

Reflecting on one of the following: the fruits, the gifts, or the symbols of the Holy Spirit, what new ideas have you formed about His character? Do you see any of these manifestations in your own life? How can the revelations of this chapter change or enhance your prayer life? Share your thoughts below:

_____

_____

_____

_____

_____

_____

_____

_____

_____

_____

_____

_____

_____

In my own reflection on the Holy Spirit, whom I had at the outset classified as a neglected part of my own spirituality, I soon realized I had been leaning on God's Holy Spirit all along. I just hadn't clearly understood this Person of the Trinity. What a gift we have been given, when God took back His Son to His right side, He sent us an advocate, faith encourager, and counselor.

I love Ephesians 1:14, which tells us that "the Spirit is God's guarantee" of our inheritance. We are the receivers of the first fruits of God's promise of this amazing eternal life with Him. It reminded me of the time my Godmother called me to her house to discuss a very important matter with me. When I arrived, she sat me down and explained that although she had no plans of leaving this earth in any hurry, her recent retirement did highlight her advancing age. She had a will in which we'd all receive a small inheritance, but she had decided it would be far more rewarding to watch us enjoy some of that now. She then handed me a check, a "first fruit," so to speak, of her labor. I was being allowed to enjoy something I did nothing to earn. It was merely by being born into her family and loved dearly by her that showed an eagerness to share her treasure with me.

That is exactly what the grace conferred by the Holy Spirit is to me, a gift from God; a gift which I did nothing to earn and do nothing special to receive. Simply by being Baptized into the family, I am entitled to this gift. It is a share in my Heavenly inheritance and a promise of even greater things to come—when the old shall pass and God will make all things new again.[20]

Through cooperation with the Spirit, I am endowed with what I need to live out my Catholic faith. In living a Sacramental life, I receive the fullness of what God has for me through the Holy Spirit. Like my Godmother, he gives it to me now while I'm still living.

---

[20] Revelation 21:4

Chapter 4
Loving God: Compassionate

¹⁶ We have come to know and have believed the love which God has for us God is love, and the one who abides in love abides in God, and God abides in him

1 John 4:16

God is Loving

Why is it important for us to see God as love? As we learned in Chapter 1, sometimes just having the knowledge, or image, of God as Father is not enough to draw us into a relationship. A relationship can be defined as the state of being connected; it is a bond or closeness. So, what is the benefit of being in relationship with God? The first thing to consider is how much richer a life lived in close proximity to God is than a life lived far away from Him.

Humans need love. We seek it sometimes like a drug—longing to love and be loved. Yet human love is flawed, conditional, and generally fails to meet all our needs. God's love is not. It is perfect, unchanging, lacks nothing and is exactly what every heart is yearning for. As Saint Augustine said, "our hearts are restless until they rest in you."[21] The love that God offers us provides rest for our hearts and fills us to a capacity we cannot fully fathom.

Our faith teaches that we were created by God "...to know Him, to love Him, and to serve Him in this world, and to be happy with Him forever in the next."[22] This might seem egocentric, unless we are knowledgeable of Scripture, where we learn that we love God because He first loved us.[23] Are you a parent? What are your expectations of your children? What did your parents expect from you? Does it seem unreasonable for God to desire us to love Him? Given what we know about His character, this abundance of love makes sense. Time spent with Scripture helps us further discover the depth of this love. It is there that God reveals that the very core of all He does for us is out of love: unconditional love.

> God's love is "everlasting": "For the mountains may depart and the hills be removed, but my steadfast love shall not depart from you." Through Jeremiah, God declares to his people, "I have loved you with an everlasting love; therefore I have continued my faithfulness to you" (*CCC,* 220).

---

[21] Saint Augustine, *Confessions,* I, 1
[22] *Baltimore Catechism No. 3*, Lesson 1, (Q. 150)
[23] 1 John 4:19

The Character of Love

Have you ever contemplated why God allowed His human creatures to have free will? We need it so our love for Him could be freely given, of our own accord, and not demanded or forced upon us. What does this freedom of choice say about the character of God? What does it say about our role in a loving relationship with God?

Scripture Search

Look up the following verses to learn more about God's love for us. What does each teach about God's love for us?

Psalm 36:7

_____

_____

_____

Micah 7:18-19

_____

_____

_____

John 17:23

_____

_____

_____

Romans 5:8

_____

_____

_____

2 Thessalonians 2:15-17

_____

_____

_____

From the beginning, although in the Old Testament He may seem harsh and punishing, God makes His everlasting love known to us. We see God's unconditional love in abundance in the Psalms, which is amazing given the less-than-holy behavior of David with Bathsheba, Uriah, and Tamar, among others.[24] David came to see that his behavior had no bearing on how much God loved him; that God's love is steadfast and true, even when we are on rocky ground! Micah echoes that sentiment by also expressing the detachment between our iniquities and God's choosing to love each of us with such compassion and mercy.

The Apostle John's Gospel could be called the Gospel of LOVE, for he is able to describe the beautiful love of the Father for the Son and the Son for us, and through *that* love of Jesus for us, the Father's love for us. John was the youngest Apostle, so perhaps it was his innocence that allowed him to be so open to receiving Jesus' love. John understood that God loves us, and that Jesus was sent as a sign of that love.

John had truly come to know and rely on the love God had for him, and to share that with us, so we may be able to do the same. Or, perhaps it was all the time John spent with Mother Mary after Jesus' Ascension that allowed John to internalize and express this divine love. Mary knew Jesus better than anyone; I can only imagine that Mother Mary shared a great of deal of her proudest memories of Jesus with John. Although John spent time with Jesus, no one knows a person like his mother—especially this Mother, who spent so much time with her Son. In John's gospel one can experience a more intimate knowledge and insight of Jesus.

Here is what I find the most amazing part of this entire scenario— in learning about Jesus, we learn about God the Father. In seeing how loving, kind, and compassionate Jesus is through John's words, we see how the Father is also all of these things. Jesus tells us, "Truly, truly, I say to you, the Son can do nothing of Himself, unless it is

---

[24] 1 Samuel 16–1 Kings 2

something He sees the Father doing; for whatever the Father does, these things the Son also does in like manner.[25]

Some Scripture verses describe a reciprocal role for us in receiving God's love, such as to "know, recognize, and understand therefore that the Lord your God, he is God, the faithful God, who keeps covenant and steadfast love and mercy with those who love him and keep his commandments, to a thousand generations."[26] It is very clear that it is not reliant upon what we give. Our participation only enhances the relationship; it does not make God's love for us any stronger. That is already at maximum capacity!

Just for a moment, ponder that thought. God cannot possibly love you anymore than He does at this very moment. It is unconditional. God can see your faults and failings, and none of it changes His love for you. Even if you choose to walk away from faith, to disregard the teachings of Scripture and Tradition, to deny the work of salvation by His Son—He still loves you beyond measure. As Saint Paul tells us, "For I am convinced that neither death, nor life, nor angels, nor principalities, nor things present, nor things to come, nor powers, nor height, nor depth, nor any other created thing, will be able to separate us from the love of God, which is in Christ Jesus our Lord."[27]

---

[25] John 5:19

[26] Deuteronomy 7:9

[27] Romans 8:38-39

Journaling

What was your reaction as you first read each of the verses describing God's love for you? As you read, were you able to accept this as true for *yourself* and not merely for other people? Take time to consider your understanding of and acceptance of God's love in your life. Did you realize it was so intense and intimate?

Despite my endless hours of Bible study and church activities, I still felt very distant from God. I longed for a warm, squishy love feeling that I anticipated when I learned God was an adoring Father. As someone who struggles with expressing and receiving human love, it was not really a surprise to me that I was not "getting it" when it came to the divine love God has for me!

That led to a meeting to talk with my priest, whom I greatly admire and see as having a very close relationship and friendship with Christ. He doesn't simply perfunctorily recite the Eucharistic Prayer each Mass, but lives the Consecration, his voice often cracking as he raises the Host and proclaims, "My friends, this IS Jesus!" I know he feels it, and appears to really "get it." I wanted the secret and I wanted what he has. As I sat with this amazing priest, I cried and begged to know how do I truly feel God's love?

He looked me in the eye and asked, "Allison, when are you going to let God love you?" That stopped me in my tracks. Let myself be loved? You mean I had to cooperate in this? Not cooperate, he explained, but allow. At that moment, sitting in his small office, I truly had no answer.

At home, I sat in my window seat and tried to visualize, as Father had suggested, a meeting with God. This was not easy. It probably took me close to an hour to get centered and relaxed. Finally, an image started to form. I saw God on the couch, His arm around me, and we were cuddled together—it reminded me of when I was a young girl cuddling with my Dad watching NASCAR or football on Sunday afternoons. In that moment, a feeling of otherworldly warmth started to envelope me and a spark was ignited in my heart.

Unfortunately, moments later I was interrupted by my son and I had to abandon my perch to attend to his needs. It was hours before I could return to the window seat and try visualizing myself with God again. This time it only took seconds. I closed my eyes and there we were, still on the couch. I was still under His protective wing. He had NOT moved. I felt the message in my heart, now bursting with emotion, "See, I'm right here, I did not move, I am not going anywhere." It was at that moment that I began to truly fall in love with God, the Father!

The experience of God's love will be different for everyone. Our Heavenly Father relates to each one of us in a deeply personal, deeply intimate way. Spend some time getting to know just how God is trying to relate to you.

Chapter 5:

Trusting God: Submission

Trust in the LORD with all your heart
And do not lean on your own understanding.
In all your ways acknowledge Him,
And He will make your paths straight.

Proverbs 3:5-6

God is Trustworthy

God is my trust. When I prayed for guidance on how to define trust, the Holy Spirit led me to www.dictionary.com. Here is what I found waiting for me there:

> "4. a person on whom or thing on which ones relies. *God is my trust.*"

There it was, clear as day: *God is my trust.* Certainly, we can rely upon the people who God places in our lives, but ultimately, God alone is the One, the True One, in whom to put your faith.

What is Faith? The author of Hebrews describes it this way: "Now faith is the assurance of things hoped for, the conviction of things not seen."[28] That same chapter provides amazing examples of people who exhibited great faith throughout Biblical history. One such example is Abraham, who brought his only son, Isaac, to the top of the mountain to be sacrificed, believing that God would be true to His word, who promised, "I will surely bless you and make your descendants as numerous as the stars in the sky and as the sand on the seashore. Your descendants will take possession of the cities of their enemies."[29]

How does one become confident in what is hoped for, or sure with their whole heart that the promises of God are true and will be received? To be certain of the things we cannot see seems impossible when we realize how difficult it is to even be certain of those things we can see! It appears as if God is asking a great deal of us. Why doesn't He simply let all who believe see, and then we'd be 100 percent sure and certain? Ah, but then we'd miss out on the gift of faith; the gift of learning to trust in the Lord with all our heart, mind, soul, and strength, and most importantly, the lesson of not leaning on our own understanding of truth, but instead holding on to hope in God.

---

[28] Hebrews 11:1

[29] Genesis 22:17 (New International Version, 1984)

Is it possible that our human feelings hinder our ability to trust God? Do past experiences of broken promises with humans unwittingly prevent us from building a relationship with God? Do we fall into a trap of not differentiating God's qualities from those of man; forgetting that although we are made in God's image and likeness, we lack His divinity? God is perfect. His love, His compassion, His mercy, and His trustworthiness are all perfect. He cannot abandon, leave, or forsake us.[30] We can trust in Him.

> *"Give us"*: The trust of children who look to their Father for everything is beautiful. "He makes his sun rise on the evil and on the good, and sends rain on the just and on the unjust." He gives to all the living "their food in due season." Jesus teaches us this petition, because it glorifies our Father by acknowledging how good he is, beyond all goodness. "Give us" also expresses the covenant. We are his and he is ours, for our sake. But this "us" also recognizes him as the Father of all men and we pray to him for them all, in solidarity with their needs and sufferings.
>
> *CCC, 2828-2829*

---

[30] Hebrews 13:5

The Character of Trust

What does the word *trust* mean to you? Can you think of someone in your life about whom you would say, "I completely trust this person?" How do you put your trust in God? Do you feel you trust with all your heart, or do you still hold back?

_____

_____

_____

_____

_____

_____

_____

_____

_____

_____

_____

_____

_____

_____

_____

Scripture Search

In the following verses, what benefits can come from putting your trust in God:

Psalm 9:10

_____

_____

_____

Psalm 28:7

_____

_____

_____

Jeremiah 17:7

_____

_____

_____

2 Corinthians 1: 8-10

_____

_____

_____

Hebrews 10:35-36

_____

_____

_____

Trust is hard to earn. Take, for example, the parent/child relationship. For trust to develop between a parent and her child, the child must experience his needs being fulfilled by the parent time and time again. With newborn babies, this trust seems almost inborn. But, as I discovered as an adoptive mother, the process can be painstaking. My daughter was over three years-old when we adopted her. She rejected me as her mother for more than three weeks. It required patient endurance on my part—fulfilling her every physical need until she finally saw me as trustworthy. Even as she saw the physical manifestations of my efforts—that I was making sure she was fed, clothed, and bathed—it still took time. How much more difficult, then, is it with the seemingly unseen actions of an invisible God? I cannot fully comprehend the faith necessary to embrace a completely trust in the Lord. Yet I know that God has equipped each of us with it.

Scripture supports this idea by illustrating over and over again that if you trust God, you are blessed in so many ways. Trust in God allows you to experience His faithfulness, love, and mercy, as well as the sense of never being abandoned or forsaken. God will prove it if we only give Him the chance. But alas, how many of us are really willing to stick it out to the end when we are in the middle of the suffering and doubt? If we are new to trusting in God, perhaps we should rely on the example of others who put their trust in Him. Then we can prepare ourselves to believe God is exactly who He says.

King David knew it was better to put trust in God than man, for men are prone to be swayed by temptations of the flesh. After David committed adultery and then murder to hide his sin, he put his trust in God's promise of forgiveness, coming before Him with a contrite heart. God not only forgave him but actually referred to him as a "man after His own heart."[31] Do you need more examples of those who put their trust in God and were blessed? Read all of Hebrews 11. Also, witness the testimony of trust displayed by Abraham, Sarah, Moses, Enoch, Noah, and Isaac in Genesis, just to name a few!

---

[31] Acts 13:16-22

The Apostle John recounts Jesus' teaching of the light; that He had come so those who believe would not have to live in darkness. To receive this promise, all we are asked to do is trust. Jesus didn't say, if you do good things, you'll be worthy of the light and free from darkness.[32] Jesus merely says trust (and sin no more). We are reminded of this by Saint Paul in his letter to Timothy. "Ignore the false teachings, focus only on the truth which has been given to us through generations of those who saw and believed, and the even greater who did not see, yet believed."[33]

We are called to have patient endurance, holding onto hope, based on what we know of God to be true. We are called to keep doing what is right, regardless of the suffering, remembering that God will never fail us. We are called to trust with all our heart, remembering that God's ways are not ours, and that they are higher.[34] We are called to recognize, know, and acknowledge God in all our being and doings. He will show us the way which we are to go according to His perfect plan for us. In short, we are called to say, "God is my trust."

---

[32] John 12:46
[33] John 20:29
[34] Isaiah 55:8-9

Journaling

Can you think back on a time in your life when you felt abandoned by God? Perhaps there was a time when perhaps you considered your trust in Him misplaced? Can you, through the gift of hindsight, see how this trial or test may have played a role in increasing your trust in God? If not, why?

_____

_____

_____

_____

_____

_____

_____

_____

_____

_____

_____

_____

_____

To me, trust is something people earn by showing their reliability, over time, in our relationships. I am cautious by nature but very open to give people a chance. It was sort of the same way when I decided to give my life to God. I believed in His innate goodness, but still wanted Him to prove it. I found myself praying for many things with the same sentiment at the core of each prayer. "I want to let this go to you, God, but I am just not sure how to completely trust in You."

So began the routine of my praying and His showing His faithfulness in my life. I prayed; He responded. Did I always get what I asked for? Absolutely not! God is a loving parent, after all, and he would never give me everything I request. He is prudent and wise, allowing what is good for me and what is necessary for what He cares most about: my sanctification. Did I recognize that immediately? Definitely not! It has only been with the gift of hindsight that I fully comprehended his trustworthiness. It is when I look back over my journal entries or contemplate the past week, month, or even year, the growing bond of trust becomes evident. One of my favorite lines in Scripture is, "I walk by faith and not by sight."[35] When we cannot see what is happening to us as the answer to a prayer, remaining faithful to God and trusting in Him can become very difficult. However, when we endeavor to trust, we discover that God will not disappoint us.

When I began to make the journey back into my faith, it did not come without great trepidation. I knew that I would have to put away some of my current behaviors and choices. One of my biggest struggles was letting go of gossip. Oh, I never called it *gossip* back then. I could've rationalized anything that I was saying under the guise of conversation, venting, or looking out for the well-being of another. To me it was therapeutic, just blowing off steam, or meaningless chatter with friends that wasn't harming anyone. I never thought of the ramifications of the person finding out, and how I might feel if someone was doing the same to me, or even more importantly, how it would affect my relationship with God. I just enjoyed it, and quite

---

[35] 2 Corinthians 5:7

honestly felt it was one of my greatest attributes. I felt it made me popular, funny, and powerful. I loved that people thought of me as "the go-to girl," or as always being "in the know" and I even have to admit, I would get a rush of adrenaline from these gossip sessions.

When I began to learn more about Jesus and His teachings, it became painfully clear that this gossip was a sinful behavior. How could I have missed this—it's not like it was hidden in some obscure text! Nope, it is a Commandment! Those nine words, "Thou shall not bear false witness against your neighbor,"[36] nearly derailed my complete reversion. I did not want to let that part of me go. I thought I wouldn't have anything to say. I did not think I'd be funny any longer, or that I could remain popular without engaging in this behavior.

I truly struggled with giving over this area of my life to God. I did not trust that He had a better plan for me. I didn't trust that there was more to me than what I knew about other people. And I didn't trust that the plan that God had for me was greater than the one I had for myself. The reformation of this part of my personality came with many starts and stops. In the end, many of my fears did come true. I did lose friends, or I guess they would be better called "acquaintances." I did sit, silent, at many social events because I had nothing to say. The uncomfortable feeling that was now part of my new awakening eventually made it impossible for me to participate in some gatherings. My whole life was about to change. If I had not seen the example in Scripture of those who trusted Him before me, or reflected back on the situations God had certainly guided me through, I could have never made this significant change in my life.

For me, I see trust in the rearview mirror. I am not always able to see what God is doing at the time God is doing it. I struggle with great anxiety, and even fear sometimes, as I work through God's plans and give up my will for His. Yet, I can open my Old Testament and look at Hannah who prayed for a baby and was given Samuel on the promise that she would give him back to the Lord when he was weaned. Then, without knowing what God had planned, she

---

[36] *CCC*, 2504

obediently surrendered Samuel to the care of Eli. God's amazing plan was to later bless this infertile woman with 5 more children.[37] Or, I can look at the faith of Juan Diego, a simple Aztec peasant, who bravely went before the bishop to request a church on the hill for the Lady in the vision. He returned to her for proof when the bishop asked, believing she would give it, and dutifully, humbly relayed her response. The Virgin Mary's apparition and Juan's trust in God and his faith to share it, whatever the cost, would bring about the conversion of the entire country of Mexico.

I think it can be very scary, especially for women who often have so many commitments to keep and roles to juggle, to "let go and let God." It took time and grace for me to trust God enough to allow Him to be in control of my social life so I could break my sinful habit of gossiping. But once we do, we realize that His plans for us are always better than our own plans could ever be.

> Your duty will be to trust completely in My goodness, and My duty will be to give you all you need. I am making myself dependent on your trust: if your trust is great, then My generosity will be without limit."
>
> *Jesus speaks to Saint Faustina (from her Diary)*

---

[37] 1 Samuel 1:1-20; 2:18-20

Chapter 6

A Forgiving God: Acceptance

Be gracious to me, O Lord,
For to You I cry all day long.
4 Make glad the soul of Your servant,
For to You, O Lord, I lift up my soul.
5 For You, Lord, are good, and ready to forgive,
And abundant in loving kindness to all who call
upon You.
6 Give ear, O LORD, to my prayer;
And give heed to the voice of my supplications!
7 In the day of my trouble I shall call upon You,
For You will answer me.

Psalm 86: 3-7

God is Forgiving

At practically every Catholic wedding I have ever attended, including my own, the loving couple has 1 Corinthians 13 as one of the readings. In case you have not had the pleasure, it goes as follows, "Love is patient and kind. Love is not jealous or boastful or proud or rude. It does not demand its own way. It is not irritable, and it keeps no record of being wronged."[38] We infer that it is speaking of human love, and that which will be best for husband and wife to sustain a happy marriage, and while that is an admirable goal, it is not the full beauty of this passage. Saint Paul speaks of God's love, His perfect love—God is love.[39] God does not hold grudges; He does not harbor resentment or bitterness, or seek retribution—He is charitable.

If God is love, and love is charity, and if being charitable means forgiving, then it is only logical to conclude that God is forgiving. Yet many people have a very difficult time making that connection. Perhaps our thought process in this area is again tangled with our own human understanding of love and forgiveness. Do we struggle to believe that there cannot be "forgiving and forgetting" in certain situations? Do some of us believe that God is God after all and therefore, perhaps His standards are higher than ours? Or, if we can't always forgive and forget, clearly neither would God.

We may think a special act, sacrifice, or gift is needed to gain forgiveness. An admittance or understanding of the wrong, a truly contrite heart, a sincere apology, and promise to try not do it again should be enough. It certainly is for God. We may be asked to do penance and make restitution to right the wrong (because of God's justice) but forgiveness is freely given from God (because of His mercy). Why do we find it so hard to believe that God will forgive us? Why is it difficult to realize that no matter what we've done, He does not hold it against us? Simply put, it is because we lack knowledge of true Love and of Divine Mercy.

---

[38] New Living Translation
[39] 1 John 4:8

There is no limit or measure to this essentially divine forgiveness, whether one speaks of "sins" as in *Luke* (11:4), "debts" as in *Matthew* (6:12). We are always debtors: "Owe no one anything, except to love one another."[147] The communion of the Holy Trinity is the source and criterion of truth in every relationship. It is lived out in prayer, above all in the Eucharist.

CCC, 2845

The Character of Forgiveness

Forgiveness is truly an act of the will. To truly forgive we must let go of expectations from the one who has offended us, and rely on God's supernatural grace in the situation. Make a list of the people toward whom you are holding anger, bitterness or resentment. What would you need to let go of, for there to be healing in this relationship? This may include you, God, or another person.

_____

_____

_____

_____

_____

_____

_____

_____

_____

_____

_____

_____

_____

_____

_____

_____

_____

_____

_____

Scripture Search

There is no shortage of evidence of God's forgiveness in Scripture. For each verse, record how it is demonstrated:

Nehemiah 9:17

Psalm 32:1

Matthew 18:21-35

Ephesians 4:32

Colossians 3:12-14

As we read the Scriptures, we see example after example of God forgiving us of far greater transgressions then those done against us. Yet, we are the ones who are slow to forgive, and even slower to forget. Clearly, the God of Scriptures is merciful, kind, and truly forgiving. Our hope for Heaven certainly rests in that, for if we were held accountable for our sins as we deserve, would there really be any chance of eternal paradise for any of us?

God pours out His forgiveness; He sent His only Son to suffer and die for our sins. "God demonstrates His own love toward us, in that while we were yet sinners, Christ died for us."[40] If God waited for us to show sorrow, for us to apologize, or for us to validate His feelings of being wronged, we'd all still be waiting for the gates of Heaven to open. How amazing is His example of offering mercy purely out of love and compassion, regardless of how the other is responding. The last line of the eighteenth chapter of Matthew's Gospel makes it quite clear, we are to heed this valuable lesson, and to do the same. God is merciful, yes; but He is also just.

Thomas à Kempis speaks such wisdom with the exhortation, "Endeavor to be always patient of the faults and imperfections of others for thou has many faults and imperfections of thine own that require forbearance. If thou art not able to make thyself that which thou wishest, how canst thou expect to mold another in conformity to thy will?"[41] Realizing how sinful we are should bring all of us to our knees out of gratitude for God's endless compassion and forgiveness. How can we see God as punishing and vindictive when we recall all he has forgiven us?

Saint Paul reminds us again and again in his letters how blessed we are that Jesus has come to wash and cover our sins, to set us free, and to give us abundant peace. Once again, God demonstrates in the Scriptures His true characteristics: loving, trusting, and forgiving. If we have been shown such mercy, shouldn't we then show mercy unto others?

---

[40] Romans 5:8

[41] Thomas à Kempis, *The Imitation of Christ* (Dover Publications, 2003)

Journaling

Reflect on your attitude toward the Sacrament of Reconciliation: What sort of feelings do you encounter at the thought of going to Confession? Have you ever had a not-so-great experience? Conversely, how do you feel after a really great Confession?

We are truly blessed as Catholics to have the Sacrament of Reconciliation, not only as a means by which we unburden ourselves of our sins, but also to receive the gift of God's grace. Grace is the freely given, completely undeserved gift from God of His holiness in our life. It is not enough to receive it; we must accept it with an open heart and utilize the strength it gives us to lead a more holy life.

Let's say you have a friend, and for no special occasion, apart from your great love for him, you decide to get him a present. You bring it home, wrap it up beautifully and are so excited to share it with your friend. You know it is exactly what is needed to bring him the peace, joy, or hope he has been missing. Your role in the gift-giving is over after you hand it over and he takes it out of the box. You certainly cannot make him use it. He must do all that for himself. I see that with God's grace—freely given, all wrapped up and delivered at every Sacrament—but we need to accept, open, and utilize the gift of grace in order for it to have any value to us.

My personal preference is to refer to "Confession" as *Reconciliation.* I love the idea of being reconciled, or made right with God. It was this realization of confession as an instrument of healing that turned me from confession-chicken to reconciliation enthusiast! My love affair with the Sacrament began shortly after I made a weekly commitment to Eucharistic Adoration. My Adoration time happened to coincide with the parish's scheduled confession time. One Saturday during Adoration, I decided I was ready to make my yearly confession. I did a very thorough examination of conscience, mustered up all my courage (because I truly thought it was the scariest thing to do in the world), and went in. As usual, I stumbled through, cried, and in the end felt a hundred pounds lighter leaving the confessional.

The following week, I was again at Adoration when the priest came into the confessional. After fifteen minutes, I realized no one had yet come in, and no one was waiting. I thought I'd had a rather difficult week and I could certainly think of a few things that I'd like to get off my conscience, so I went again. Just as I had one week earlier, I stumbled through, I cried, and I felt two-hundred pounds lighter. And, strangely, this time I was filled with hope for the week ahead. The next week, again, no one was waiting. After half an hour, still no one came. "Well," I thought, "I can't let him have come here for nothing." So, back in I went.

This went on for several weeks, and although people did start to come for confession, I started to feel drawn each week to continue going myself. At times, it seemed like an addiction; I needed it, craved it, and couldn't wait for it. What was happening? Was it okay to receive this Sacrament this much? Was I abusing the sacrament? I prayed for answers but continued to go, feeling deep within me a transformation—a sense of peace, a newfound strength, and a deepening faith that I had never experienced before. God has the neatest ways of answering prayers; I had mentioned this new ritual to my Bible study group and soon after, one of the ladies came in with the funniest story. She had been watching an old *Mother Angelica Live* show on EWTN. During the show, Mother mentioned going to confession every week, basically because she only wanted to be responsible for one week's worth of junk (I'm paraphrasing). It was a huge epiphany: If Mother Angelica could go each week, if she had enough "junk" to dump each week, surely I could, maybe even should, be going every week.

As the months went on, I somehow realized that frequent confession was having a profound effect on my spiritual life, but I did not really understand how or why. One day, when I was searching for something on the Internet, I stumbled across a teaching on the Sacraments and God's gift of grace. Everything stopped. What was this I was reading? Each time I received reconciliation I was receiving grace? Suddenly, a veil lifted, and I understood it wasn't just about bringing all my junk and leaving it at Jesus' feet; it was so much more!! Each time I knelt before the Lord, shared the struggles in my life, which were truly struggles in my faith, I was being made stronger through the counsel of my confessor in the person of Christ, through the words of forgiveness given in absolution, and sanctified by God through my faith in it all. In that moment of absolution, I am given more of God's spirit that helps me to live a more holy life, to be holy because He is holy.[42] It was a life-altering discovery, and

---

[42] Leviticus 19:2

one which was there the whole time; I had simply never chosen to open my eyes to it. God wants to make me whole, and yet I had been choosing to remain in pieces.

The gift of the Sacrament of Reconciliation was also instrumental in my own journeys (yes, plural) of forgiveness. We forget, or perhaps never fully comprehended, this sacrament as one of healing. Anger, resentment, and bitterness are all poisons that sicken the spirit. A wise person once said, "Bitterness is the pill we swallow, hoping the other person will die." When we hold on to these things, we are not only hurting ourselves, but our relationship with Christ and the whole Church. In addition, the grace we receive in the Sacrament will help us grow in holiness and love: God's love. This is the supernatural love and holiness we need to forgive others as Jesus instructs us in the *Our Father,* so that we will be forgiven.

We may think that what we did is unforgivable, but God disagrees. There is nothing He can't forgive. We may think that what was done against us is unforgiveable, but God disagrees. There is nothing He can't help you forgive. Remember, forgiveness is an act of the will, and it is not easy. Yet, God has given us all that we need for whatever He asks of us. All that is required of us is to cooperate, to ask, and to be open to receive the grace necessary for His work to be accomplished.

God the Father wants what is best for His children. God the Son died so that we might be forgiven, and share eternal life with Him. God the Holy Spirit makes visible the invisible of God's working in our life. God truly is love. His works chronicled in Scripture and in our own lives prove His trustworthiness. And lastly, that we may come before Him, sinful and sorrowful, and yet receive complete absolution, illustrates profoundly that God is forgiving.

About the Author

Allison Gingras is a writer, speaker, and retreat leader. She is a wife and homeschooling mother of three: Ian, Adam, and Faith. Allison has been married to her high-school sweetheart, Kevin, for more than 22 years. She credits the sacramental grace of her marriage with overcoming the rocky soil of her early spiritual journey.

Allison began "Reconciled To You" ministries in 2009, primarily to encourage others to live out their Catholic Faith to its fullest, especially through the Sacraments. Since its founding, Reconciled to You expanded to include many aspects of living an authentic Catholic life. Through the ministry, she offers presentations, teen and adult retreats, and spiritual direction. Allison is active in social media, which she views as a tool to evangelize as well as socialize.

Allison was a contributing author to the book, *A Special Mother is Born*. In the book she shared the amazing, God-directed story of the adoption of her profoundly deaf daughter, Faith, from China. Allison is also a contributor to "TechTalk" on Catholicmom.com, where she reviews applications for the Android system, primarily as they relate to the Catholic faith or motherhood. She developed a podcast titled "Catholic 24/7," as well as a blog on her web site, to further discuss the beauty of the sacraments and their practice in everyday life.

In her "spare" time, Allison has the honor of singing at LaSalette eXtreme, a monthly evening of praise and worship, with what she considers to be the very best band "with no name."

About Leonine Publishers

Leonine Publishers LLC makes fine Catholic literature available to Catholics throughout the English-speaking world. Leonine Publishers offers an innovative "hybrid" approach to book publication that helps authors as well as readers. Please visit our web site at www.leoninepublishers. com to learn more about us. Browse our online bookstore to find more solid Catholic titles to uplift, challenge, and inspire.

Our patron and namesake is Pope Leo XIII, a prudent, yet uncompromising pope during the stormy years at the close of the 19th century. Please join us as we ask his intercession for our family of readers and authors.

Do you have a book inside you? Visit our web site today. Leonine Publishers accepts manuscripts from Catholic authors like you. If your book is selected for publication, you will have an active part in the production process. This book is an example of our growing selection of literature for the busy Catholic reader of the 21st century.

www.leoninepublishers.com

What Stinks?*

An Adventure In Highland Park

by Sally Valentine * illustrated by Suzanne Valentine

ISBN-10 1-886166-24-2

ISBN-13 978-1-886166-24-0

Pyramid Publishing Inc.

PO Box 8339

Utica, New York 13505

www.pyramidpublishingservices.com

To Deirdre

Stop & smell the lilacs!

Sally Valentine ♡

This book is dedicated to the glory of God
with thanksgiving for His magnificent creation.

Chapter 1

"What stinks?" asked Derrick as he walked into the classroom.

"Yeah, what stinks?" echoed Reinaldo as he filed in right behind his friend.

"Did somebody die in here over the weekend?" asked Lamar as he entered next.

"I hope you boys are not talking about my new perfume," said their teacher, Mrs. Levine. "It's called White Lilacs, and I bought a big bottle of it at Kaufmann's department store over the weekend."

"Well, I like it, Mrs. Levine," said Janie.

Reinaldo and Lamar just glared at Janie while Derrick jabbed her with his pencil. "I hope she can get her money back," he whispered under his breath.

Janie yelped when she felt the point of Derrick's pencil in her waist. "But aren't lilacs purple, Mrs. Levine?"

"Derrick, don't start the day by abusing your friend, and yes, Janie, lilacs are usually purple, but they also come in shades of pink and blue and white. In fact the reason I wore this perfume today is to tell you about our next adventure. Mayor Johnson has invited our class to

1

Highland Park to sing at the Lilac Festival this year."

"I hope nobody gets arrested," said Lamar. It was his teenage brother, Steven, who had been accused of stealing a silver candlestick on their last class trip to George Eastman House.

"Our last trip did end with an unfortunate experience," agreed Mrs. Levine, "but we learned a lot about George Eastman, and the theft taught us all something about making assumptions and how to solve a mystery. Besides I don't want it to be said that Mrs. Levine's 5th grade class at Susan B. Anthony School #27 is afraid to try a new adventure."

"But Miz Levine, singing some old dumb song to a bunch of lilacs ain't no adventure," whined Derrick.

"Isn't an adventure," corrected Mrs. Levine automatically. "Anyway, Derrick, we won't be singing to a bunch of lilacs. We are going to be Mayor Johnson's honored guests and will march in the Lilac Parade as well. After your efforts at saving the Charlotte Lighthouse by finding the Eastman Kodak stock certificates hidden in the tower wall, Mayor Johnson wants our class and The STARfish in particular to lead the parade."

The STARfish consisted of Derrick Davis, Lamar Green, Reinaldo Santiago, Janie Washburn, and Jeanetta Jones, five of Mrs. Levine's students. #27 School in Rochester, New York was a charter school that centered academic learning around co-operative groups. The groups were rearranged from time to time, but this particular group had been together since the previous school year. They had chosen their group name when studying about the Titanic. They capitalized the star in STARfish because they fancied themselves important; and in fact they had gained notoriety when they saved the Charlotte Lighthouse from being torn down and also when they solved the mystery of the stolen candlestick at George Eastman House. They always seemed to be right in the middle of all of the action whether it be inside the classroom or out.

Mrs. Levine would have liked to say that the STARfish were her best students, but in fact they were not. Jeanetta always completed her homework and never got below an A- on any test, but the others were in some ways her most difficult students and the least co-operative, at least with each other. Derrick and Janie had been assigned detention more times that she could count. But if Mayor Johnson wanted them to lead the Lilac Parade, then who was she to argue?

Derrick looked at Lamar. Lamar looked at Reinaldo. Reinaldo looked at Derrick. They still weren't sure if it was cool to be seen with a bunch of lilacs.

"Probably those ladies we saw at Mr. Eastman's house will be there wearing their purple blazers," grumbled Derrick.

"Did I mention that the whole parade and the singing afterwards will be carried live on TV on the RNEWS station?" said Mrs. Levine.

"Well, why didn't you say so?" said Reinaldo. The boys became much more enthusiastic, although Derrick wanted to know if the real lilacs would smell as bad as Mrs. Levine's perfume.

"I may have overdone it a little bit with the perfume this morning," admitted Mrs. Levine, "but I wanted to get your attention."

Derrick thought that being slapped upside the head might have been a less painful way to get his attention, but he wisely kept that thought to himself. He had promised his mama that he would try to do better in school, and he didn't want to aggravate Mrs. Levine too much. She might start in on one of her lectures. Derrick had a theory that teachers got paid an extra $100 for every lecture they gave their students. He thought that Mrs. Levine must have been getting rich on the lectures she gave because of him alone.

"Maybe we could open the windows just a little bit," said Jeanetta diplomatically.

"What will we wear in the parade?" said Janie.

"Why, we'll wear our yellow T-shirts with the bumblebee logo for Susan Bee Anthony School #27," said Mrs. Levine. "What else would we wear? Of course, we'll be representing our school. Besides, I want to be able to find you, and the yellow will stand out nicely against the purple and green of the lilacs. Now if you'll all take your seats I have some information for you to read about Rochester, Highland Park and the lilacs."

"Great," muttered Derrick under his breath. "I knew any new project would mean more work for us."

"Was that you, Derrick, volunteering to start reading aloud to the class?"

"No, Miz Levine, I was just telling Reinaldo that we certainly would be learning a lot." Once again Reinaldo

looked at Derrick and Derrick looked at Reinaldo. Then they both looked at their desks to avoid laughing.

Mrs. Levine settled her 5 foot 10 inch frame and her 179 ½ pound body into the chair at her desk. Not that her students knew these statistics. They only knew that she could be very imposing, especially when standing directly over one of their desks. Nor did they know her age. When asked, she always said, "I'm on the sunny side of 50," whatever that meant.

"Debra, why don't you start reading for us?" Mrs. Levine asked after she got comfortable, and another week in Room 217 had begun.

Chapter 2

On Tuesday there was an e-mail message from Granny Rob at the Sunny Hill Nursing Home in Kalamazoo, Michigan. Miss Brenda Robinson was lighthouse keeper Cuyler Cook's great-great-great-niece and the sole heir to the Kodak stock certificates that had been found in the Charlotte Lighthouse. Those stock certificates were now worth a fortune. Miss Robinson used the money to restore the lighthouse, but she had also been very generous to Mrs. Levine's class. She bought them a state of the art computer for their classroom complete with software, laser printer, and even a photo scanner. She also bought them cameras last fall (Kodaks of course) when they studied photography. Miss Robinson bought herself a computer as well and found an aide at the nursing home to teach her how to use it.

Since she had no children or grandchildren, Miss Robinson told Mrs. Levine's students to call her Grandma Robinson and started an e-mail correspondence with them. Grandma became shortened to Granny and Robinson to Rob so now her messages were signed "Love from Granny Rob."

Jeanetta had e-mailed Granny Rob yesterday about their upcoming visit to the Lilac Festival and she e-mailed back. Everyone was allowed to use the computer when his or her class work was done, but sometimes it seemed that Jeanetta was the only one who ever finished her work. The kids had lobbied Mrs. Levine for separate e-mail accounts, but she held fast to the idea of having only one account for the whole class to use. The truth was that Mrs. Levine still trusted books more than she trusted computers, and she wanted to take this one slow step at a time. She logged on first every day, and if the message was for a particular student, she printed it for them and then deleted it. It was up to them if they wanted to share it with the class. Jeanetta asked to read hers aloud.

Subj: Lilacs
Date: April 3, 2000
From: Grannyrob@sunnyhill.org
To: Levine217@27susanbee.edu

Dear Jeanetta,

Your e-mail about the Lilac Festival brought back pleasant memories for me. I visited Rochester once in 1934 or was it 1935? My memory's not so good anymore. My father bought a brand new Ford coupe, and he and I drove there all the way from Kalamazoo in one day. It took eighteen hours, and we stopped four times along the way to eat the bologna and mayonnaise sandwiches that Mother packed for us. I never wanted to look at another bologna sandwich after that. Anyway, I remember meeting a dapper young man at the pansy bed who escorted me all around the park. Daddy didn't like that very much, but I felt like a queen. Yessir, I'll always remember Rochester and the lilacs. Michigan has lilacs too but not all together in a beautiful place like Highland Park.

Love from Granny Rob

"What's a coupe?" asked Janie.

"It's a car, jer... I mean, Janie," answered Derrick.

"Yes, it's a car that was popular back in the 1930's" said Mrs. Levine as she glared at Derrick. "That's even before I was born. Maybe Granny Rob still has a picture of it that she could send to us."

"Gee, Mrs. Levine," said Jeanetta "why don't we buy Granny Rob some of that White Lilacs perfume and send it to her?"

"That's a great idea, Jeanetta. If everyone contributes fifty cents, we could buy a nice big bottle to send her."

"We better warn the nurses first," whispered Derrick to Lamar.

"What's that Derrick? I thought you were getting used to the smell of my perfume."

"I am Miz Levine. I was just joking." As his teacher turned back toward the chalkboard Derrick looked back at Lamar and rolled his eyes.

"Now I'd like to make a list on the blackboard,"

"Greenboard," interrupted Derrick. This time he grinned at Lamar. Mrs. Levine was an old-fashioned teacher who still called the chalkboards blackboards although they were all now green.

"Okay, Derrick, I'd like to make a list on the greenboard of everything you've learned about Highland Park and lilacs so far," said Mrs. Levine. "Just call out a fact and I'll write it down."

"The lilacs in Highland Park were planted by John Dunbar," began Jeanetta. "He grew them from plants that were originally from the Balkan Mountains, and they are a symbol of good luck."

"Where are the Balkan Mountains?" asked Janie.

"They're in Bulgaria which is in Eastern Europe near Kosovo and Serbia. I looked it up on the map."

"What else do you know smartypants?" sneered Derrick.

"Highland Park was started in 1888 with twenty acres of land donated by Mr. Ellwanger and Mr. Barry from their nursery. It was Rochester's first city park." began Jeanetta.

"What's an acre?" asked Reinaldo.

"Didn't the kids at the nursery need the land for a playground?" asked Lamar.

"Those are both good questions, boys. Can you answer them Jeanetta?"

"Well, I'm not sure how big an acre is, but this nursery was not a nursery for children. It was a nursery for plants," said Jeanetta.

"Jeanetta's right as usual," replied Mrs. Levine. "A nursery is a place to look after young living things. It can have plants or children. An acre is a piece of land about as big as our whole schoolyard. So picture in your head a piece of land twenty times as big as our schoolyard. Does anyone except Jeanetta know how many acres of land Highland Park has now?"

"I do," said Lamar as everyone looked at him in surprise. They expected Jeanetta to know all the answers, but not Lamar. "It's 155 acres."

"How'd you know that?" said Derrick suspiciously.

"That's easy. My house number is 155."

"Oh," said Derrick with relief. He was afraid for a minute that his friend was turning into some sort of nerd.

"So now picture in your head a piece of land 155 times as big as our schoolyard. That's how big Highland Park is now."

"I don't think my brain stretches that far," moaned Reinaldo.

"Stretch your body to stretch your mind, I always say," said Mrs. Levine reaching for the ceiling with her arms. Stretch along with me, class."

"Yes, Mrs. Levine," parroted the class as they reached for the ceiling too—anything to get up and move around a little.

"Now who designed Highland Park?" asked Mrs. Levine turning again to the green chalkboard.

"I don't remember his name, but it's the same guy that designed Central Park in New York City," said Tomas. "I went there when I stayed with my aunt last summer."

"His name was Frederick Law Olmsted."

"Hey! His initials spell FLO."

"So they do," said Mrs. Levine. Now no one has any

excuse for not remembering that name. Mr. Olmsted designed Highland Park to have a very natural or un-designed look. I'll give extra credit to anyone who comes in tomorrow with the name of a different park Mr. Olmsted designed.

"Who knows how old Highland Park is?"

"I do," said Janie. This is 2000 and Highland Park was started in 1888 so 2000 minus 1888 is 112. Highland Park is 112 years old." Janie smiled at Mrs. Levine and Mrs. Levine smiled at Janie. Janie was hoping that now that she had given an answer Mrs. Levine would ignore her for the rest of the lesson and she could go back to daydreaming.

Mrs. Levine was thinking about how happy she was that this lesson included math as well as geography, history, and current events. She just loved it when that happened. Now to sneak in some language arts. She went back to the board and wrote Flour City and Flower City.

"What cities am I talking about class?"

"Well, the Flower City must be Rochester since we're talking about lilacs," answered Jeanetta, "but I don't know what the other one is."

"Anyone else want to guess?"

"Buffalo."

"New York City."

"Moscow."

"Moscow?" Mrs. Levine let out only a small sigh. "Maybe I just better tell you that this was a trick question. The Flour City is also Rochester, or was Rochester. From 1823-1849 Rochester was called the Flour City, that's f-l-o-u-r City because at that time it was the largest flour producing city in the world. There were 20 flour mills here that produced 500,000 barrels of flour a year.

"Think of all the pancakes we could make!" said Reinaldo.

"You're right, Reindaldo. That would make an awful lot of pancakes," said Mrs. Levine. In 1850 Rochester became the Flower City, that's f-l-o-w-e-r City, because Mr. Ellwanger and Mr. Barry started the largest nursery in the world here."

"And they're the ones who gave the land to Highland Park," said Janie.

Mrs. Levine beamed. "I'm so happy when my students remember things.

"Hey. Flour and flower are some of them homophones," said Lamar.

Mrs. Levine's smile got wider. This was going to be a great day.

And so it was. Before anyone knew it, the clock said 3:20 P.M., dismissal time.

Chapter 3

On both Wednesday and Thursday some time was spent discussing what songs to sing at the Lilac Festival. The girls wanted to sing the love song from the Titanic movie, but the boys vetoed that. Reinaldo wanted to do "Livin La Vida Loca" by Ricky Martin, but Mrs. Levine protested. "Our classroom is loca enough as it is," she insisted. Mr. Barnes, the music teacher, wanted them to perform "Lilac Time," a song by Rochesterian Dorothy Louis, but the choir from East High School was performing her whole musical, "How Lilacs Came to Rochester."

"What about 'The Fifty Nifty United States?'" suggested Janie.

The class thought about it for a minute. Then Reinaldo said, "I guess that would be OK." He didn't want to admit to liking too much any song he had learned in school, but in reality the boys as well as the girls liked reeling off the names of the states as quickly as they could in that song.

"How about 'Take Me Out To The Ballgame?'" said Lamar. He had been to the opening day of the Rochester

Red Wings and still had that song running through his head.

"That might be okay," said Mr. Barnes. "The Red Wings are also associated with spring in Rochester even though they play at Frontier Field instead of Highland Park."

"They'll probably have us singing 'take me out to the lilacs' instead of 'take me out to the ballgame,'" whispered Derrick to Lamar.

Unfortunately Mrs. Levine, like most teachers, was equipped with supersonic hearing and replied. "That's a great idea, Derrick. Let's make up another verse to 'Take Me Out To The Ballgame' that has to do with Highland Park and the lilacs. I'm putting you in charge, Derrick."

Me and my big mouth, said Derrick to himself. Mama always says it's my mouth that gets me into trouble.

That day at lunch even Derrick's friends couldn't help but tease him about his assignment.

"Have you written your song yet, Derrick?"

"Sing to us about the lilacs, Derrick."

Derrick got so disgusted that he took his lunch tray over to the corner and ate with Grandma Smith, the lunch lady.

Jeanetta finally took pity on him and dropped down on the bench next to him when the rest of the class went outside to the playground. "Why don't you e-mail Granny Rob and ask her to help you write a new verse to the baseball song? She'd probably be good at that. Mrs. Levine said you were in charge. That doesn't mean you have to do the work yourself. It means that you're the boss."

"Yeah, I'm the boss," said Derrick.

Jeanetta ran off to join the others outdoors. She didn't hear Derrick say in the softest voice possible, "Thanks, Jeanetta."

After lunch Derrick finished his work in record time and ran over to the computer and began to type.

Subj: Song
Date: April 5, 2000
From: Levine217@susanbee.edu
To: Grannyrob@sunnyhill.org

Dear Granny Rob,

I need help!!!!!!!!! Have you ever heard of the song "Take Me Out To The Ballgame?" Well, mean Levine put me in charge of writing a new verse to that song that has to do with lilacs and Highland Park. Can you think of anything? Write me (I'm Derrick Davis—one of The STARfish) back.

Derrick was disappointed on Friday when there was no message from Granny Rob, but on Monday it was waiting for him when he entered the classroom.

Subj: Song
Date: April 9, 2000
From: Grannyrob@sunnyhill.org
To: Levine217@susanbee.edu

Dear Derrick,

I've had so much fun trying to help you with song

lyrics. I've been asking everybody including Dr. Howard my heart doctor, Sue Ellen my hairdresser, and Mrs. Patterson the cleaning lady, to give me ideas. Here's what I've got so far.

Won't you come see the lilacs?
They're here in Highland Park.
Walk up and down around the hills,
You may find pansies and daffodils.
For its sweet, sweet, sweet things you'll smell here.
Lilacs are fragrant you see.
And its blue, pink, purple and white,
They're the lilac trees.

Now I know lilacs grow on bushes not trees, but I needed something to rhyme with see. They call that poetic license I think. Tell me if you like it, and don't call your teacher mean. You don't know what a mean teacher is. I had Miss Bartholomew in the one room school, and she used to hit us with the ruler and make us stand on one foot in the corner when we were misbehaving. I swear that's why I still lean to the left when I walk. Now that was one mean teacher.

Love from Granny Rob

"I've got it Miz Levine!" shouted Derrick as he ran to the front of the classroom with the copy of Granny Rob's e-mail. He quickly folded back the part of the e-mail about Mrs. Levine being mean.

"Got what, Derrick?"

"The words for the lilac song. You said I was in

charge. That means I'm the boss, so I asked Granny Rob to help me. Are these OK?"

Mrs. Levine quickly scanned the sheet. "These are perfect, Derrick. And lilacs can be called trees. Highland Park is actually an arboretum, a tree garden. Why, there are 300 species of just conifers in Highland Park, not to mention the horse chestnuts, magnolias, maples and other trees. And you're right. I didn't say you had to do it all by yourself. Why didn't I think of asking Granny Rob?"

Because you're not as smart as Jeanetta, thought Derrick, but this time he was smart enough to keep his thoughts to himself.

Chapter 4

It was 10:15 A.M. and the class had finished singing the new words to "Take Me Out To The Ballgame" several times when Janie burst through the classroom door shouting, "Mrs. Levine, Mrs. Levine, look what I brought to school!" Janie was carrying a big cardboard box with several holes poked along each side.

"Good morning to you, too, Janie. Why are you late, and what's in the box?"

"We...ll," said Janie very dramatically. "It's my new pet skunk." She pulled open the box flaps and reached into the box.

"Take that right outside this very minute," said Mrs. Levine sternly while backing away from the box.

Derrick and Reinaldo ran to open the windows. "This could be worse than the perfume," mumbled Reinaldo.

"It's OK, Mrs. Levine. It's really OK. Let me explain," begged Janie.

"All right, Janie. I'll listen to your story, but put that box out on the fire escape while you talk." Mrs. Levine heaved one of her notorious sighs as she sank all 179 ½ pounds into the nearest chair. Mrs. Levine had years ago established herself as the best sigher in all of Susan B. Anthony School #27. Her students and former students had taken to rating her sighs on a scale of 1 to 10. Today's sigh was a 9. The only sigh that had rated higher this year was when Steven was accused of stealing the candlestick from George Eastman House. That sigh went off the scale at 15.

"I'll be back in a minute, Princess," said Janie into the box as she folded the flaps back in place, reached over the window sill, and gently dropped the box and its contents onto the fire escape. All eyes were on Janie as she slowly strode to the front of the room. "We...ll," she began again. Janie just loved being the center of attention. "It all started Friday night. Me and Dad went out to Pizza Hut for dinner and then stopped for ice cream at Friendly's on the way home. Dad had a big fire and had to work late at the firehouse so..."

"Janie, it's Dad and I, and maybe you could cut out some of the details and get to the important part of the story," interrupted Mrs. Levine as she heaved another sigh (only a 3 on a scale of 1–10).

"I'm trying to tell you, Mrs. Levine, that it was late when Dad left the firehouse where he works and he was worried about me being home alone. You know that this is the first year that I can stay alone after school though usually Mrs. Battaglia is home upstairs, but on Friday she went shopping with Angela—that's her granddaughter."

Mrs. Levine wanted to scream at Janie to get to the

point but was afraid that interrupting her again would only lengthen the story rather than shorten it. Instead she heaved her third sigh of the day and sat back to listen.

"So Dad was hurrying to get home and forgot to take off his big black rubber boots at the firehouse. When he finally got home he took them off and left them outside the door because they were still wet. Then we went out to dinner. Did I tell you that we went to Pizza Hut?"

At this point the students were getting restless too. "Janie, what about the skunk?" blurted out Reinaldo.

"But that's what I'm trying to tell you."

It was Reinaldo's turn to sigh as Janie continued. "When we got home from dinner it was dark outside. Angela was visiting her grandma and came down to show me the new Nikes her grandma—that's Mrs. Battaglia—bought her. We went outside and I put on my dad's boots, pretending that I had new shoes too. That's when I found Princess."

Princess? Lamar mouthed to Jeanetta who shrugged in return. She was hurt that her best friend Janie hadn't told her anything about this. After all, isn't that what a best friend is for?

"When I put my foot into Dad's boot, I felt something soft and furry. I dropped the boot and screamed. Then Angela screamed. Mrs. Battaglia heard us, and she screamed too. Dad came outside, but he didn't scream. Dad said, 'Stand back,' and he tipped the boot upside down and out fell Princess. Well she wasn't Princess yet. She was just a baby skunk—the cutest little baby you've ever seen. You'll think so too when I go outside and get her. Can I bring her in now Mrs. Levine?"

"Not so fast, Janie. A skunk is a wild animal, and wild animals can have rabies."

"Rabies!" shouted Reinaldo as he jumped up and headed for the door. "Poison ivy was enough for me. I don't want any rabies."

Mrs. Levine stood up and intercepted Reinaldo at the door. "Calm down, Reinaldo. The skunk cannot hurt you out on the fire escape. And we can call someone from Animal Control to come and take it away."

"Take it away?" shouted Janie indignantly. "You can't take Princess away. She's OK. She's really OK."

"All right, Janie. I'll let you continue with your story, but it better include a trip to the vet." Mrs. Levine sat back down and heaved sigh number four.

"Oh, it did, Mrs. Levine. That's why I'm late. Me and Dad just picked her up from the vet right now."

Mrs. Levine automatically said, "Dad and I" under her breath and Janie continued.

"Dad wouldn't let me touch her and made her stay outside in the boot all night. He thought her mama might come back for her. But Princess is just like me— she has no mother." This last sentence was spoken in a whisper. Janie wiped away one tear with the back of her hand and continued. "I hardly slept all night. Mrs. Battaglia let Angela stay over with me in The Palace, and we took turns guarding Princess from the window."

"What's The Palace?" asked Debra. Twenty-two pair of eyes glared at her.

Derrick spoke for the group. "Don't ask questions. We'll never hear the end of the story."

It was too late. Janie looked at Debra and responded. "The Palace is what I call my bedroom. My Grandma Washburn bought all the curtains and bedspread and stuff for it. Everything is pink and white with lots of ruffles and lace, real girly. I would have liked denim or even purple, but she didn't ask me. I didn't want to hurt Grandma's feelings so I didn't complain. It just doesn't seem like home to me, so I call it The Palace."

"Anyway, on Saturday morning Dad said I could keep Princess if the vet said it was OK. I only had to beg him nine times and promise to keep my room clean for a year. We brought Princess to the Northside Animal Hospital, and Dr. Dugan the vet said that she didn't have any diseases. She operated on Princess to take out the stinky glands, and she was ready today. Dad thought she might like to live at school better than at home so he dropped us off."

"I'll bet he did," said Mrs. Levine still wearing a dubious expression.

"Is Dr. Dugan a lady vet?" asked Tomas. "I've never met a lady vet."

Janie gave him a disgusted look. "Yes, she's a lady, Tomas. This is the new millennium. Get with it."

"Let me just call Dr. Dugan," interrupted Mrs. Levine. "Janie, find me her number. The rest of you start working on your vocabulary worksheets while I investigate this further."

Chapter 5

Fifteen minutes and two sighs later, Mrs. Levine hung up the phone. "I guess its time for us to see this creature, Janie," she said. "You may bring Princess into the room now. Students you may stop working on your vocabulary for a few minutes."

If Mrs. Levine had bothered to glance around the room she would have seen that nobody needed to stop working on the vocabulary worksheets. They had never even started working on them in the first place. All ears had been listening to Mrs. Levine's side of the conversation, and all eyes had been on Janie who was still standing in the front of the room with fingers, arms, and legs all crossed in hope.

After Mrs. Levine's okay, Janie let out a "yippee," uncrossed her body and clamored over to the window to retrieve her precious package. She sat it on her teacher's desk, but after a nervous glance at Mrs. Levine, decided to put it on the floor. All of the other students were straining out of their desks to see. Janie ceremoniously opened first one flap and then another and another. She reached into the box and gently picked up her new friend and cradled her in her arms.

At that point, most of the kids left their seats and ran up to touch the black and white ball of fur. In all of the commotion Debra tripped over a chair leg and bumped into Lamar, who elbowed Anthony, who stumbled into Derrick, who pushed Janie, who fell over as her arms flung open and she dropped her furry friend. As she fell with a small plop onto the wooden classroom floor, four paws and one tail quickly emerged from the ball. Princess blinked her eyes a few times and ran directly to the nearest corner of the room.

Everyone seemed to be talking at once.

"Derrick, how could you hit me like that?"

"I didn't mean to hit you, Janie. Anthony hit me."

"Grab her before she runs away."

"Somebody close the door."

"Don't anybody step on her."

"EVERYBODY BACK TO YOUR SEATS. NOW!"

The students slowly walked in the direction of their chairs while still trying to keep their eyes on the scared newcomer in the corner. Princess now had her little head down and her back arched. She was frantically moving her front paws back and forth as if trying to dig a hole in the unyielding wood floor, while at the same time backing further away from the group. Suddenly she turned around, lifted her tail high in the air, and squeezed her muscles together in a futile effort to spray her perceived enemy.

Some of the class pinched their noses, others ducked their heads under their desks, and even Janie took a step backwards in anticipation of smelling that famous skunk odor. They all seemed a little disappointed when

the only odor still floating through the room was from Mrs. Levine's White Lilacs perfume.

"Thank God for veterinarians," said Mrs. Levine.

"Does that mean we can keep her here in Room 217?" asked Janie, a big grin forming on her face.

"We'll keep her at least for today. But every animal including skunks needs some recuperation time after surgery. We'll let Princess rest in her box for the rest of the morning. After lunch I'll let everyone get to know Princess, but only one at a time so she's not frightened."

"Why did you name her Princess anyway?" asked Derrick.

"Well, actually it was Angela who named her Princess. She said that if she lived in The Palace with me we should call her Princess."

"What if it was a boy?"

"Well, then we would have called him Prince."

Janie scooped Princess back up in her arms and carefully carried both the box and the little fur ball to the back of the room. Then she came back to sit next to Jeanetta, who turned her back and looked the other way.

"What's wrong with you?" Janie whispered to Jeanetta.

Jeanetta didn't respond and kept looking in the other direction.

Mrs. Levine sank down into her chair while heaving the seventh sigh of the day. She opened her bottom desk drawer and took out her bottle of Tylenol. "Debra, would you please bring me some water?" was all she said as the students reluctantly turned back to their vocabulary worksheets.

Chapter 6

The next few weeks blew by like a cool breeze. Princess quickly fell into the school routine and became a celebrity at School #27. The kids in Mr. Bernard's class across the hall were envious. Gabriella, their pet cockatiel, was no longer the star of the school.

Princess spent the mornings in Room 217, mostly sleeping in her box, as the kids did their academic work. Even Mrs. Levine had to admit that she was a quiet pet. She accompanied them to the cafeteria for lunch where Grandma Smith, the lunch lady, provided her with matching pink bowls for her food and water. She also found a pink and white placemat to set them on. The placemat sat on the floor, of course, and the students took turns feeding Princess canned dog food or pieces of mystery meat from the school lunches. No one, including Janie, wanted to go outside and hunt for the dead mice, grubs, and beetles that skunks normally eat. Any attempts to get Princess to secretly eat broccoli, peas or beans from a passing lunch tray were usually unsuccessful. Princess seemed to hate the green vegetables as much as the kids did.

At recess, Princess went outside on a leash with the class and rooted around for slugs and cutworms while they shot baskets or jumped rope. In the afternoons Princess visited the other classrooms along with two students who could explain to the new class all they had learned about skunks. Mrs. Levine said that if they were going to have a skunk in the classroom, they at least were going to use it as a learning experience. When the bell rang at 3:20 P.M., Princess went back in the box for the trip home. She spent the rest of the evening in The Palace with Janie.

Mrs. Levine let the students work in groups to do research on both of their projects—Highland Park and skunks. She had started to switch the students in each group, but decided to keep The STARfish intact because she could better keep an eye on them if they were altogether. She was also hoping that working together would patch up the quarrel that Janie and Jeanetta seemed to be having.

On Tuesday The STARfish learned that the hills and valleys of Highland Park were created thousands of years ago by glaciers, but that the lilac didn't become the official flower of Rochester until 1948. In between lessons Janie invited Jeanetta over after school to help take care of Princess, but Jeanetta said she had too much homework to do. Janie didn't know how Jeanetta could have homework when she didn't and they were in the same class, but that was Jeanetta. She did homework even when there was no homework.

On Wednesday they learned that skunks could get to

be thirty inches long, weigh about ten pounds, and move very slowly. They can't climb trees. In the fall they eat a lot of food so that they can spend the winter in underground dens. Derrick said that Janie belonged in an underground den, but Janie didn't even hear him. She was busy inviting Jeanetta over to watch the new video she had just gotten. Jeanetta, however, said she had to clean her room.

On Thursday they learned that some of the lilacs in Highland Park had been named after famous people. There was a deep blue lilac named after Frederick Douglass, who had published his North Star newspaper right here in Rochester. There was another blue lilac, this one the color of the sky, named after the famous aviator Charles Lindburgh. Others had been named after Presidents Lincoln and Eisenhower. And there was a creamy white lilac named Rochester. While they were working, Janie invited Jeanetta over to bake cookies as a surprise for her dad, but Jeanetta had to go grocery shopping with her mom.

On Friday The STARfish learned that there was a connection between lilacs and skunks. Skunk musk was once used as a base of perfume just like lilacs are used to make perfume today. They also discovered that the word skunk comes from a Native American word seganku, but that the skunk's scientific name is mephitis mephitis, which means bad odor, bad odor. They found out that in 1989 a purple and white skunk named Lila became the mascot of the Lilac Festival.

Janie invited Jeanetta over to go to Pizza Hut with

her and her dad, but Jeanetta was busy. She was also too busy to go to the mall on Saturday and too busy to ride bikes on Sunday. When Janie asked why she was so busy, Jeanetta replied, "I just am. Why don't you ask your new best friend Angela to go with you?"

Janie felt awful. How could Jeanetta think that Janie wanted to be best friends with Angela when everyone knew that Jeanetta was her best friend? Angela just happened to be at her house when she found Princess, that's all.

Jeanetta felt awful too. Instead of doing homework, cleaning her room, and shopping with her mother like she had told Janie, Jeanetta had actually been moping in her room.

"Why don't you call Janie?" asked her mother.

"I just can't," said Jeanetta. "She's got a new best friend," and she went back to her bedroom to mope some more.

"Why don't you call Jeanetta?" asked Janie's father.

"She hates me," said Janie, and she sat down with Princess to figure out what to do. They both fell asleep as Janie stroked Princess' silky fur, and Princess snuggled up into Janie's soft blue sweatshirt.

Chapter 7

The following Monday began with an e-mail from Granny Rob. Since it was addressed to them all, Mrs. Levine asked Deborah to print it out and read it to the class.

Subj: White Lilacs
Date: April 23, 2000
From: Grannyrob@sunnyhill.org
To: Levine217@27susanbee.edu

Dear Friends,

Thank you so much for the White Lilacs perfume. It's had quite an effect on Mr. Peters in room 207. Since I started wearing it, he's been coming by my room three times a day, and he even asked to sit next to me at the lunch table. Imagine having a boyfriend at my age! I'll invite you all to the wedding. :-) Have you memorized the words to the song yet? I can't get it out of my head. Learn a lot today.

Love from Granny Rob

Things may have been going well for Granny Rob,

but in Room 217 the feud was still on between Janie and Jeanetta. Janie had given up on trying to invite Jeanetta over, and the two only spoke to each other when they absolutely had to. Now even the boys were trying to patch things up. Every time Mrs. Levine's back was turned, Derrick went into his skunk imitation to try to make them laugh. He would stand up, move his hands like he was pawing the ground, and then turn around and stick up his butt like he was about to spray the room. The other boys howled, but he got barely a snicker out of Janie or Jeanetta. Mrs. Levine pretended not to notice.

Lamar felt really bad for Jeanetta, just as Jeanetta felt really bad for Lamar when his brother Steven was accused of stealing the candlestick. He wrote her a note and then tore it up. He didn't want her to get the idea that he was in love with her. Instead he gave her his computer time, saying that he didn't feel like using the computer anyway.

Reinaldo tried to make both girls feel better with red Twizzlers. To Reinaldo food was the answer to any problem, and he knew that red licorice was the favorite of both girls. In fact it was one of the reasons they were best friends in the first place. That, plus the fact that they both fell off the school bus into the same mud puddle several years ago. Everyone knew that Twizzlers was their favorite candy. Sometimes they each started from one end of a long piece of red licorice and had an eating race to the center, but not on this day. Janie ate her licorice without even glancing over at Jeanetta.

Jeanetta thanked Reinaldo for the Twizzlers, but gave them back to him. Reinaldo shrugged his shoulders and ate the licorice himself. After all, he had tried.

Meanwhile, practice went on for the Lilac Festival. Mrs. Levine even had them using their recess to practice marching around the school. They would be following Abelard Reynolds School #42 and the East High School marching band in the Lilac Parade, and Mrs. Levine wanted them to be able to march in time to whatever music the band played. Derrick thought it wasn't fair to use recess time for marching practice, but when he complained to his teacher she just said that life wasn't always fair. Then she started in lecturing about how marching was good exercise and helped the mind as well as the body. There goes another $100, thought Derrick.

They had also perfected their songs to the point where they all could sing them in their sleep. The hand motions were perfect too. Everyone was root, root, rooting for the home team in sync, and Maria, Justina, Jazmin and Tonya had been chosen to hold up blue, pink, purple and white lilac branches for their special verse of "Take Me Out to The Ballgame."

"Remember," cautioned Mrs. Levine, "I'll bring lilac sprigs for each of the girls to wear in her hair. Under no circumstances will any of you pick any of the lilacs in the park. Is that understood?" As she spoke this last sentence her eyes lingered in turn on each of The STARfish.

"Now I have some good news," continued Mrs. Levine. "Lamar's brother Steven will be joining us for this trip."

The room suddenly went silent. Everyone was thinking about what had happened the last time Steven went with them on a trip. Lamar looked surprised. Steven hadn't told him about this, but then Steven didn't tell him much of anything, anyway. Lamar knew that after his problem at George Eastman House, Steven had become friends with Mr. and Mrs. Levine, and that they paid him sometimes to do jobs for them. Mrs. Levine must be paying Steven, thought Lamar. He wouldn't normally hang out with a bunch of 5th graders.

Mrs. Levine was indeed paying Steven to help on this trip. She thought that an uneventful trip like this would erase the bad feelings Steven had about the previous trip. Steven wasn't so sure he wanted to do it even for money. He only finally agreed when Mrs. Levine also agreed to buy him the "garbage plate" from Nick Tahou's stand at the food court. No teenage boy could resist this special heaping platter of hot dogs, home fries, macaroni salad and beans all covered in extra grease.

"One more thing," said Mrs. Levine now that she had everyone's attention. "Princess will not be going to the Lilac Festival. Janie, promise me that you will not bring Princess along with you that day."

"I promise, Mrs. Levine, that I will not take Princess along with me to the Lilac Festival," said Janie in a voice oozing with sincerity.

Mrs. Levine sat back and smiled. "Now I'm sure I've taken care of everything."

Chapter 8

There didn't seem to be an idle person in Rochester as the final preparations for the Lilac Festival got under way. The city workers were busy painting the crosswalks and the line down the center of the parade route purple. The park workers were likewise decorating the garbage cans. Crafters and food vendors were setting up their stalls. Hotel and restaurant owners were gearing up for thousands of out-of-town visitors. Bus drivers were readying their buses for shuttle trips back and forth to Highland Park, and the police were setting up extra traffic patrols. Mayor Johnson was practicing his speech, and the musical performers, both amateur and professional, were running through their numbers one last time.

The lilacs also were doing their part, promising to be at their peak right on Lilac Sunday. This was no easy task since the dates for the Lilac Festival had to be set almost a year ahead of time, and nothing was more unpredictable than the weather in Rochester, New York. A really cold April could prevent the lilacs from blooming until June, while an unusually hot April could cause the lilacs to bloom too early. In that case the festival goers would be looking down on dead lilac petals rather than up at beautiful purple blossoms. But this year things looked perfect, and the only thing that could ruin the flowers now would be a combination of strong winds and torrential rain, unlikely, but not impossible. After all, it had been known to snow on Mother's Day in Rochester.

Janie woke up extra early on parade day. She had laid out her black shorts and her yellow Susan Bee T-shirt the night before so that she would not be late today. She even cleaned up her white sneaks with her dad's help, but he had sent her downstairs to Mrs. Battaglia for advice on what to do with her hair. Usually she and Jeanetta fixed each other's hair, but not this time. Jeanetta's mom had shown Janie how to braid cornrows into Jeanetta's coarse black hair, and Jeanetta had learned just how to use the curling iron on Janie's fine, straight light brown hair. Oh, how Janie wanted her best friend back even though they looked and acted so very differently.

Janie ran back upstairs after Mrs. Battaglia had fashioned her hair into a makeshift bun. She wanted time to say good-bye to Princess and explain to her why she had to stay home today. "You can't come to the Lilac Festival, Prin…," began Janie. But as she looked into Princess' sad eyes, Janie's heart began to melt. I know I promised Mrs. Levine, she thought, but I just can't leave Princess home alone. She looked at her book bag. She looked back at Princess. She looked at the book bag. She looked back at Princess. Then with one quick move she scooped Princess up, tucked her inside her book bag, and ran back down the stairs just as the school bus pulled up to the curb.

All the way to school, Janie worried about how to get Princess to Highland Park. I promised Mrs. Levine I wouldn't bring Princess to the Lilac Festival. I promised Mrs. Levine I wouldn't bring Princess to the Lilac Festival. That sentence kept racing back and forth in Janie's mind. I promised Mrs. Levine that I wouldn't bring Princess to the Lilac Festival. That's it, thought Janie. I promised Mrs. Levine that I wouldn't bring Princess to the Lilac Festival, but I didn't promise her that somebody else wouldn't bring her. Now, let's see... Janie reached for her hair to twirl like she always did when she was working out a problem, but thanks to Mrs. Battaglia, there was no hair there to twirl. I've got to get my best friend back, thought Janie for the second time that morning.

Chapter 9

By the time Mr. Rodriguez swung the big yellow school bus into the bus loop and opened the door, Janie had a plan. Walking into the classroom as casually as possible, Janie passed by Reinaldo and Derrick without even an insult. She smiled when she came to Jeanetta's desk and saw Jeanetta already seated with her backpack on the floor next to her. Normally Mrs. Levine made all of the students hang their backpacks in the closet with their coats, but today being a special day, they were allowed to keep them at their seats. Because they would be carrying their lunches and props for the songs, Mrs. Levine was letting them take their backpacks with them on the bus to Highland Park.

Getting Jeanetta to ignore her was not a problem for Janie because Jeanetta had been turning her back on her former friend for days now. This morning, when Jeanetta saw Janie entering the classroom, she quickly turned and started talking to Debra. Perfect, thought Janie.

As she walked by Jeanetta's desk, Janie shrugged her right shoulder and allowed her backpack to slip to the floor, as if by accident. Nobody paid attention as she casually bent over to retrieve it. After all, Janie dropping things and retrieving them was not an unusual occurrence. Nobody noticed that when Janie stood up it was not her own purple backpack that she was carrying but Jeanetta's purple backpack. Best friends should have the same kind of backpacks, shouldn't they?

So far so good, thought Janie, as she sank quietly in her seat. If anyone noticed that Janie was being a little too quiet, they didn't mention it. Janie was thinking about the brilliance of her plan. Not only would Princess get to the Lilac Festival, but, when Jeanetta found out that Janie had chosen her to be the one to carry her precious Princess, she would have to forgive her. Then they could be best friends again.

Janie was so lost in her own thoughts that she didn't realize that everyone else's attention was riveted to the door. Lamar's brother Steven had just slouched in.

Steven was nineteen and worked evenings at the Mini-Mart on Norton Street. Some of the students had not seen Steven since their last trip when he had been unfairly accused of putting a silver candlestick from George Eastman House in his pocket. Now here he was and wearing the same gray hooded sweatshirt with the big pockets.

The room went silent. The silence lasted for only about fifteen seconds, but it was one of those fifteen seconds that seem like an hour. Finally Jeanetta, who found the photograph that proved Steven innocent, called out, "Hey, Steven."

Steven grinned. "Hey, Jeanetta. What's happening,

guys? Look. My pockets are empty." He pulled both pockets of his sweatshirt inside out, revealing nothing but lint. Everyone laughed, and the tension was gone. Then Mrs. Levine almost tripped in her hurry to get up from her desk to welcome Steven.

"I'm so glad you're here, Steven. Now let me go over the rules for the day one more time, and we'll be ready to leave. Janie, I'm so glad I don't see Princess here with you."

I'm glad you don't see her too, thought Janie as she smiled back at her teacher.

Chapter 10

Mr. Barnes, the music teacher, was waiting out in front of the school, his pitch pipe just visible over the edge of his shirt pocket. His music stand was already loaded onto the bus. Derrick was surprised to see Mr. Bernard's whole class on the bus as well. "What are they doing here?" he said to Reinaldo in what he thought was a whisper, but, of course, Mrs. Levine with her supersonic hearing had honed in on his complaint.

"Now, Derrick. Don't you remember me telling you that Mr. Bernard's class was going to the Lilac Festival, but only as spectators and not as participants? It was just the right thing to do to offer them a ride on our bus since we have so many extra seats."

Derrick who could feel a lecture coming on was sorry once again that he had opened his mouth. Luckily for him, and anyone else who had ears, Mrs. Levine had no time for another lecture. She simply waved her group onto the bus, and they were off.

Janie, like a mother hen, was still worried about her little Princess. She had left the zipper of her book bag open about two inches so that Princess could breathe.

But what if that wasn't enough? And what if someone happened to look into the bag and saw one of Princess' eyes staring back at him? And what if...

"Janie, sing." Mr. Barnes was ordering Janie to participate with the rest of the group. He insisted that they use their time on the bus constructively by warming up their vocal cords. Mr. Barnes was almost as bad as Mrs. Levine, thought Derrick. Maybe she was tutoring him on the side.

Mrs. Levine looked up when she heard Mr. Barnes speak. It wasn't like Janie to be so quiet. Maybe she wasn't feeling well. Not wanting to interrupt Mr. Barnes, she made a mental note to check Janie's forehead for a fever when they got off the bus. Meanwhile, she joined the class in singing "Won't you come smell the lilacs?"

"I do smell the lilacs!" yelled Reinaldo. Everyone stopped singing and started laughing. Reinaldo had been sitting up front with the window open. As the bus turned the corner from Goodman Street onto Highland Avenue, the sweet smell of the lilacs was suddenly everywhere. As were the people.

Moms, dads, kids, teenagers, grandmas and grandpas were all jockeying for a place along the parade route. There was even a delegation from St. John's home, wheelchairs up against the curb, waiting for the festivities to start. A city policeman waved Mr. Rodriguez onto one of the park roads where he quickly unloaded Mr. Bernard and his class. Then it was off again to the Science Parkway where parade participants were lining up.

Janie mentally said a quick goodbye to Princess as she filed off the bus with the rest of her class. Mr. Rodriguez would be taking the bus along with the backpacks to the South Avenue parking lot where they would meet later. Janie also said a silent prayer that Princess would be good, but she had no need to worry. Between the darkness of the backpack and the silence of the now empty bus, Princess simply curled up and went to sleep. At least for a while.

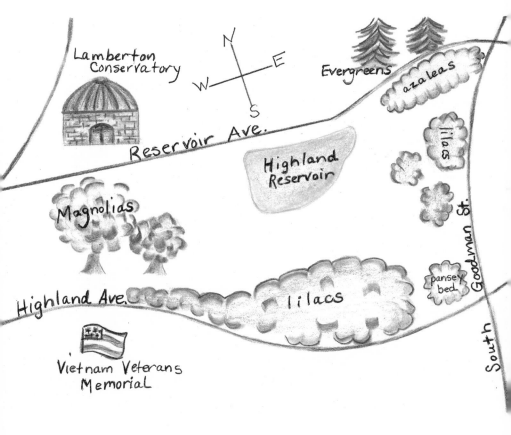

Chapter 11

"Where's Mayor Johnson? You promised he would be here," said Derrick. He considered himself the mayor's best friend ever since they met last year while rescuing the Charlotte Lighthouse.

"I'm sure he's here," replied Mrs. Levine, "In fact, there he is now."

They looked up to see Mayor Johnson waving at them from the back seat of a big purple Cadillac whose white convertible top had already been lowered. He looked still dressed for the office in a black suit and white shirt, although he did have on a light purple tie.

"Don't run in front of his ca...," cautioned Mrs. Levine, but her words were too late. Her students had already started swarming around the unusual vehicle like the bees that they wore on their shirt logos. It was as if Mayor Johnson were wearing a suit made of honey. Even Steven, who was too cool to show any enthusiasm, kept reaching out to touch various parts of the car.

"Good morning, friends," said Mayor Johnson with a big smile. "I'm so happy to see you and even happier that you're wearing those yellow t-shirts. I had no trouble picking you out in this crowd. Did you notice my lilac colored tie? My wife made me wear it. Mrs. Levine, would you let The STARfish ride in my car with me? I'd like to have you all ride, but this car just won't fit everybody. I'm sure my co-workers from City Hall won't mind getting out to walk with the rest of you."

"Oh, the mayor brought his posse," said Steven to no one in particular as the mayors aides reluctantly got out of the car.

Mrs. Levine knew that three fourths of her class would hate her, but not any more than Mayor Johnson's aides seemed to hate him at the moment. She simply nodded, and Derrick, Lamar, Reinaldo, Janie, and Jeanetta scrambled into the back seat and up onto the convertible ledge. Janie and Jeanetta chose to sit on opposite sides. Mayor Johnson raised his eyebrows at Mrs. Levine, and she simply shrugged as a reply. Although she was still ignoring Jeanetta, Mrs. Levine was glad that Janie seemed to have gotten over whatever was bothering her on the bus.

"How about this gentleman over here?" said the mayor while pointing in the direction of Steven. Steven looked behind him to see who the mayor was pointing at, and seeing no one, realized that he was the gentleman in question. "Are you part of this group too?"

"That's my brother, Steven," said Lamar proudly. It wasn't often that he was proud to be Steven's brother.

"Why don't you sit in the front seat with the driver, Steven, while I ride back here with the kids? You all can help me throw out candy to the spectators on the sidewalk."

Steven murmured, "Uh, OK," in the direction of the mayor, but could hardly contain a grin as he opened the wide Cadillac door and slouched on in. The crowd slowly parted as the driver slipped the car in gear and eased down the parkway to the lead spot at the front of the parade. If this car only had my sound system, Steven was thinking. Then I could really dig it.

Meanwhile Mrs. Levine gathered the remaining members of her class and Mayor Johnson's entourage from City Hall into their place in line behind the East High School marching band and in front of the Basset Hound Society.

"No fair!"

"How come they get to ride and we don't?"

"Why do The STARfish get to do everything?"

The complaints were coming from every direction at once. In fact the kids were so busy complaining that they didn't even ask to pet the dozen basset hounds that were walking on leashes behind them

Mrs. Levine instinctively reached into her pocket for her bottle of Tylenol, but immediately remembered that she had left it on the bus. Then, emitting a long sigh (7 on a scale of 1–10) she lifted her head, looked straight ahead and started marching in time with her students.

Chapter 12

The parade came off almost without a hitch. There was one tense moment when two of the basset hounds just sat down and refused to walk any more, but the owners scooped them up and carried them the rest of the way. And there was only one close call when Reinaldo threw his candy with a little too much vigor and almost fell head first onto the pavement. Luckily Janie saw him and grabbed the back of his yellow t-shirt just in time.

"You saved my life! You saved my life!" a grateful Reinaldo kept saying.

"It's okay, Reinaldo. I just didn't want to have to stop the parade or get blood on my white sneaks. My dad's a firefighter and he saves lives all the time." Except for my mom. He couldn't save her life, thought Janie, but I'm not going to think about that now.

When the parade ended, Mayor Johnson had his driver drop The STARfish at the South Avenue lot where Mr. Rodriguez had moved with the bus. He waved and went to meet up with his entourage saying, "I'm looking forward to seeing you on stage this afternoon."

Mr. Rodriguez met them in front of the bus. "Are you ready for lunch? You look awfully hungry."

"Oh, my God! I forgot about lunch," moaned Janie.

"How could you forget about lunch?" asked Reinaldo. He never forgot about any scheduled meal or the snacks in between either.

Reinaldo didn't understand. "Jeanetta," Janie said quickly. "Let me get your lunch out for you."

"No way," said Jeanetta as she stepped right by Janie and onto the bus to retrieve her own lunch.

"Please, Jeanetta. Let me get it for you. I want to be best friends again," Janie pleaded.

Jeanetta just kept walking down the bus aisle.

"Don't!" said Janie as Jeanetta reached her hand toward her seat on the bus. Janie had run onto the bus right behind Jeanetta and now intercepted her hand just as she was about to touch one of the purple book bags.

"What's wrong with you, Janie? Let me go."

"It's, uh, it's just that this morning our backpacks got switched uh by uh mistake. This one is mine and that one is yours. Here I'll get it for you."

"I'll get it myself," said Jeanetta dropping Janie's backpack and stomping off to get her own. "You're up to something, Janie Washburn, but leave me out of it. And I better not be missing anything from my backpack." With that she turned and ran back off the bus.

Meanwhile, Janie unzipped her backpack a little more and peeked in at Princess. "Did Jeanetta hurt you, baby?" she cooed to Princess. Reassuring herself that Princess was all right, Janie reached in further to get her peanut butter and mayonnaise sandwich and to find her apple. The sandwich was still intact, although a few black and white skunk hairs clung to the plastic wrap. It was the apple that looked different. It had more than a few bites taken out of it. "That's okay," said Janie. "I don't mind sharing my lunch with you, Princess."

As Janie walked down the bus stairs she heard Derrick, Reinaldo, and Lamar all laughing at her.

"Was that you talking to your sandwich?" sneered Derrick.

"Did it answer you back? Did it say, 'don't eat me?'" asked Lamar.

"How'd you eat that apple already?" said Reinaldo. "I thought I was the fastest eater in the whole fifth grade."

"Drop dead!" said Janie. "So what if I was talking to my sandwich. It has more brains than the three of you boys put together."

The boys kept laughing, and Janie looked around for a place to sit. Jeanetta was sitting next to a blue lilac bush with Steven, and Janie knew she wasn't welcome there. She finally sat by herself on a rock near a white lilac bush. Maybe I shouldn't have brought Princess along after all, she thought.

Janie's reverie was interrupted when Mr. Barnes and the rest of the class burst into view. Mrs. Levine trailed several hundred feet behind them.

"Sit here and rest your feet, Mrs. Levine," said Mr. Rodriguez jumping up.

"Don't mention feet," Said Mrs. Levine with a big sigh (9 on a scale of 1–10) as she sank to the ground.

"Mr. Rodriguez would you be so kind as to go with Steven to the Nick Tahou's tent. I promised him a 'garbage plate,' and I like to keep my promises. I think I'll just sit for a while. I'm glad to see that everything is so calm and quiet around here."

Chapter 13

The students were sorry when lunchtime came to an end. Mrs. Levine had been too tired to look after them, and they'd had a great time chasing each other in and out of the lilac bushes and up and down the small hills. With the exception of a few tulips missing some petals, Highland Park was none the worse for all their fun. Meanwhile Janie was having her own version of fun. She had sneaked back onto the bus to spend some more time with Princess.

After a half hour rest and some kettle corn, Mrs. Levine got back her energy and took charge once again.

"Students I want you to pick up all of your trash and anything else you see laying around. This world would be a much better place if everyone just picked up after himself, I always say."

She couldn't believe it when Derrick sprang right up and started scrambling around, looking for trash. He's starting to really respect me, she thought. She would have been disheartened to know that Derrick could feel another lecture coming on, and picking up litter beat listening to a lecture any day.

"One, two, three..." Mrs. Levine, like all good teachers, always counted her group at regular intervals while on field trips. "Eleven, twelve,...twenty, twenty-one. Twenty-one? We're missing somebody. Who's missing?"

"It's Janie," said Jeanetta. "I saw her go back on the bus."

Mrs. Levine looked quizzically at Jeanetta. For someone who said she didn't want to have anything to do with her friend, Jeanetta always seemed to know where Janie was. "Derrick, go see if Janie's on the bus."

Jamie heard Derrick call her name, and quickly stuffed Princess back in her book bag. After giving her a last little kiss on the nose, Janie stood up to see Derrick standing right in front of her.

"Oh, now you're kissing your book bag too? Wait 'til I tell the boys about this," said Derrick. He ran as Janie chased him off the bus.

"I'm starting to worry about you, Janie. Are you sure you're all right?" asked Mrs. Levine.

"I'm fine," replied Janie truthfully.

"Fine for a crazy person," added Derrick, but Mrs. Levine chose not to hear that. She was busy lining everybody up for the walk over to the Conservatory Stage where they would be performing.

Chapter 14

While the students walked, Mr. Rodriguez pulled the bus around to Reservoir Avenue behind the Conservatory Stage.

Mrs. Levine dismissed all of the kids' protests that they should ride on the bus, too. She said, "Exercise the body, and you also exercise the mind. Besides, this way we get to see and smell all of the lilacs and experience some of the other rooms here in Highland Park. See if you can spot the entrance to Poet's Garden. If an old lady like me can walk so can you."

"Rooms?" said Lamar to Derrick. They looked at Mrs. Levine like she had been out in the sun too long. Because the park looked so natural, they had forgotten that Mr. Olmsted had designed the park with many separate areas or rooms where visitors could feel totally away from the hubbub of city life. The rooms were connected by small openings that were to entice people to explore what lay beyond their vision.

The class arrived at the stage just in time to see Mayor Johnson drive up, still being chauffeured in the purple Cadillac. The Vice Mayor and his other assistants looked happy to be riding again.

"Hello again," said the mayor, hopping out of the car like a teenager. "I told you I'd come by to introduce you to the crowd and to hear your performance. Derrick, I hear that you're the one responsible for some new words to an old song."

"Him and Granny Rob," answered Jeanetta before Derrick had a chance to speak.

"Yeah, me and Granny Rob," echoed Derrick while looking at Jeanetta with poison in his eyes.

"Well, let's begin then," said the mayor. "It looks like we have a good crowd." Indeed, all of the bench seats were full, and the extra people were spread out over the lawn.

Mayor Johnson walked up the steps leading to the stage and addressed the audience. His assistants stood off to the side of the crowd. The sun bounced off his shiny black shoes and the small bald spot that was forming in the middle of his coarse black hair. "Good afternoon, everyone, and welcome to Rochester's eighty-first Lilac Week. I'm sure that this year's festival will go down in history as being one of the best, and one that will be remembered by all for a long time to come. Now I'd like to introduce some of my favorite children, the fifth grade class from Susan B. Anthony School #27 and their teachers Mrs. Levine and Mr. Barnes. I'd also like to introduce my special friends The STARfish who helped rescue the Charlotte Lighthouse last year and who helped catch a thief at George Eastman House this fall. Derrick, Lamar, Janie,

Jeanetta, and Reinaldo take a bow. I hope we won't be having anything that exciting here today, but I know this group will entertain you well. Let the show begin!"

The students filed single file onto the stage and sorted themselves by height into rows as they had been taught. Mr. Barnes strutted to the front of the stage and spread his music on the music stand. He blew into the pitch pipe, and the concert was underway. What a colorful sight! The students in their yellow t-shirts, with sprigs of lilacs in strategic places, looked like another glorious bed of flowers that had been temporarily planted in Mr. Olmsted's beautiful park. With the sun shining down, the wind wafting the smell of lilacs and the students swaying in time to the music, the effect was intoxicating.

I'll remember this day for a long time to come, thought Mayor Johnson as he sat back and reveled in the sights and sounds. Truer words were never thought nor spoken.

Chapter 15

The first "Eek!" came from Donald's mother who was sitting on the lawn behind the last row of benches. It was almost drowned out by the students' singing. Mr. Barnes heard it but believed that no matter what the audience did, one must go on with the show.

The second, third, and fourth "eeks" were harder to ignore, and the following screams were accompanied by the sound of people getting up and running away.

We don't sound that bad do we, thought Derrick. He was really trying to do a good job and looking at Mr. Barnes. After all this was his song they were singing.

Even Mr. Barnes could not ignore this, and he threw down his baton in disgust.

Janie's eyes became as big as Oreo cookies as she finally glanced behind Mr. Barnes and saw a black and white furry creature calmly walking straight toward Mayor Johnson.

"Oh, Princess, why couldn't you stay on the bus?" said Janie out loud. I must have left the zipper open too far, she thought.

One look at Janie confirmed Mrs. Levine's worst

fears. Janie couldn't look at her teacher. She imagined fire coming out of Mrs. Levine's nostrils and steam pouring from her ears. Trying to make the best of a bad situation, Mrs. Levine sprang up and called out, "It's all right everyone. Don't panic. This is a pet skunk that belongs to one of my students. She's been de-scented and won't hurt anyone. Janie come down here right now and get your pet."

Princess was now about six feet away from Mayor Johnson, who had resisted running with the rest of the audience. Some of his posse had run with the rest of the crowd and some were hovering in the background. "It's okay, Janie," he said. "I have a way with animals. I'll pick up your pet for you." He inched forward toward the scared animal, trying not to frighten it. "Everyone stay back."

But the black and white beauty was frightened. She lowered her head. She raised her tail. She arched her back.

"I'm outta here," yelled Reinaldo as he bolted from the stage.

"Remember she doesn't smell anymore," said Janie to the few remaining onlookers.

The skunk acted as if she didn't hear. She stamped the ground with her front paws. Then she stamped the ground some more. Mayor Johnson inched closer and closer to the escapee. She stamped the ground faster. "I've got her," said the mayor reaching out his arms toward the frightened creature who, at the same exact moment, turned and let loose her spray, hosing the mayor and everything else within a ten foot radius.

Mayor Johnson stumbled backwards and fell to the ground in a coughing fit. His eyes started to water and the heat of his anger blazed red through his dark brown skin. "I thought you said she was de-scented," he managed to choke out in between coughs. "Someone help me." His posse started running around in circles.

"Sh-she i-is," stammered Mrs. Levine. "I mean she w-was. I mean I th-thought she was. I mean I don't know what happened. JANIE! What's going on here?"

Janie didn't answer. She was chasing Princess, who was waddling as fast as she could go toward an underground den below the outdoor stage. When she was within grabbing distance of the furry creature, Janie clapped both hands over her mouth stifling a scream.

"That's not Princess. That's not Princess. Princess' white stripe is wider than this one. Where is Princess?"

"Yes, Janie, where exactly is Princess?" demanded Mrs. Levine. I think Mayor Johnson and I would both like to know. The mayor nodded while still wiping the tears away from his eyes. One of his assistants was running over with a wet towel.

Janie did not have to answer, for at that moment Jeanetta appeared. She was walking toward the group with Princess cradled in her arms. Jeanetta had deduced that the spraying skunk could not be Princess, but knew that if Janie believed that it was Princess, then the real Princess must be close by. Then she remembered Janie's strange behavior with the book bags and ran back to the bus to investigate. There she found Princess still curled up asleep. She now presented Janie with the notorious pet.

"Thanks, Jeanetta," Janie whispered. As both girls stood cuddling the little darling, it looked as if the feud might be over.

Chapter 16

One by one, the students and parents who had fled were now returning to the scene of the crime. They congregated in a little group, keeping their distance from Janie and Princess. Mrs. Levine had just finished delivering a lecture to Janie, and everyone was afraid to speak directly to her or to Mayor Johnson. However, that didn't keep them from whispering among themselves.

"I wonder if Janie will get suspended," said Debra's mother.

"Maybe she'll get expelled," answered Anthony's father.

"What if Mayor Johnson gets the police to take Princess away?" worried Lamar.

"What if she goes to jail?" said Derrick. From the look on his face you couldn't tell if he would be happy or sad about that outcome.

Then Janie started to speak and the others stopped talking and edged closer to listen.

"But, Mrs. Levine, I don't know why you're so mad. It wasn't Princess who sprayed Mayor Johnson. It was some ole other skunk. That's not my fault. I don't own the park. This is the mayor's park isn't it, and that makes that skunk his skunk doesn't it? Mayor Johnson got sprayed by his own skunk then didn't he? My Princess wouldn't do that."

"Oh boy, Janie's going to get it now," muttered Reinaldo.

"Janie, you, yourself, thought it was Princess at first. I could tell by the look on your face. That's what made me tell the mayor that the skunk was safe," answered Mrs. Levine through clenched teeth. "Otherwise he wouldn't have gotten so close. Besides, you broke your promise to me. You promised that you would not bring Princess along on our trip to Highland Park. Have you forgotten about that?"

"But I kept my promise. I didn't bring Princess along on the trip—Jeanetta did. She carried Princess here in her backpack."

"Janie Washburn, I hate you!" screamed Jeanetta. "Now you're trying to blame me for this."

"I'm not blaming you, Jeanetta. I'm just explaining to Mrs. Levine that I technically didn't break my promise to her. I thought you'd be happy that I chose you to carry my precious Princess."

"Happy? Happy? I hate you! I'll never be friends with you again if I live to be six hundred and forty-five and a half years old." She stomped her foot and moved away.

"Enough discussion. Janie, I want you to go over there and apologize to Mayor Johnson. RIGHT NOW."

Janie, while still clinging tightly to Princess, slowly started walking toward the mayor. The mayor's posse had reassembled, but they weren't standing very close. One of his aide's was feeding him tissues from her purse behind her back while her face was turned in the other direction. Another one was running around, flapping her arms saying, "This is awful. This is awful." The Vice Mayor looked like he was trying not to laugh. The closer Janie got, the stronger the skunk odor was and the more she wanted to hold her nose. But she sure didn't want to start Mrs. Levine lecturing again. She stopped about three feet from the mayor and spoke into Princess' fur.

"I'm sorry, Mayor Johnson."

"I don't think he could hear you, Janie. I know I couldn't."

Janie lifted her head an inch. "I'm sorry, Mayor Johnson."

"Try again."

She lifted her whole head up. "Okay. Okay. I'm sorry. I'm sorry."

The mayor rose, still dabbing at the corner of his eyes with the tissues. "I accept your apology, Janie, but I hope you'll forgive me if I don't feel like getting too close to either you or Princess right now."

"I think I'll have to throw away these clothes," he said while stripping off his tie and shirt. "Actually, I didn't like this tie anyway. My mother-in-law gave it to me last year for Christmas, and my wife made me wear it today."

"Here, Mayor." Steven stepped out of the background and slouched over to the mayor. "You can wear my sweatshirt. It's a little dirty—it got some of that hot sauce on it—but at least it don't smell like no skunk."

"How thoughtful you are," said Mrs. Levine.

"Ain't nuthin'," said Steven. "The mayor, he's the man." He lifted one long arm to slap five with the mayor and extended his other arm to wrap around Janie.

"And I'll try to keep this little girlfriend out of trouble for you."

"You like Princess don't you, Steven?

"You know I do, Janie, but if I was you I'd get Princess right back on that ole bus before anything else can go wrong."

Janie nodded and went to move in that direction. She stopped when she heard Derrick yelling, "Look, everybody, here comes that newspaper guy Ron with his camera. I wonder if he wants to take my picture."

Mrs. Levine sighed (10 on a scale of 1–10) in total defeat. "This is just perfect. Now we'll be the laughingstock of the whole city of Rochester."

"You're lucky it's just me," said Ron. The TV cameras left a half hour ago so they could get the videotape from the parade edited for tonight's local news. I heard the screams, but I was over at the Viet Nam veterans' memorial, and it took me a few minutes to get through the crowd. Someone headed for the Frederick Douglass statue told me what happened. Then I just followed the smell and here I am. I'm sorry, Mayor, but this is a story I just can't pass up. Would you mind posing with these young people and that naughty skunk?"

"Princess is not nau...," Janie started to reply, but one

look at the mayor and she changed her mind.

"Too bad the newspaper's not scratch and sniff. Then the readers could get the full effect," said Ron laughing at his own joke. "Take a bath in tomato juice, Mayor. I hear that works for dogs," he continued, still amused. "There. This picture ought to make the front page. See you all later." He waved and ran back the way he had come.

"We'll talk later, Mrs. Levine. I think my police escort is here now to take me home," said Mayor Johnson.

"Tell them to roll down the windows," advised Derrick.

"I expect the rest of you to go back to work," the mayor yelled to his cohorts from City Hall.

"Yes, Mr. Mayor," they said in unison.

Chapter 17

It was a subdued group of students that boarded the bus back to school. Mrs. Levine was too tired and angry to make them sing or do any type of learning activity.

Mr. Bernard's class had been in the audience, had witnessed everything, and was now whispering among themselves.

"I bet Mrs. Levine will never let Janie bring Princess to school again. Now our cockatiel, Gabriella, will be the star of the school like she deserves."

"Yeah. Mrs. Levine won't be bragging about her precious STARfish any more either."

"Yeah, I'm tired of them always getting to do everything."

Mr. Bernard was thinking that he should tell them to be kinder, but he was tired of Mrs. Levine's class always in the limelight too; so he just sat back and fell asleep.

Mr. Barnes sat staring out the window. He looked like he might cry. He had never had a performance ruined by a skunk before.

Janie, at Mrs. Levine's insistence, put Princess back in her own backpack and set it on her lap.

Jeanetta had taken a seat as far away from them as possible.

Derrick, Reinaldo, and Lamar were sitting in the back with Steven.

They were almost back to school when Derrick broke the silence by yelling, "What stinks?"

"Don't start that again, Derrick," warned Mrs. Levine. "You know I don't want to hear one more word about skunks or how they smell."

"It's not a skunk, Mrs. Levine. It smells more like old garbage or rotten eggs."

By the time he had these words out of his mouth, the new foul odor had seeped forward, and other students began holding their noses and complaining.

"Oooo! That's sick."

"Who died?"

"I think I'm gonna throw up."

Lamar, who had been sitting quietly, suddenly realized the source of the new odor. "It's Steven," he yelled out. "He's passing enough gas to launch the next space shuttle."

The groaning continued.

"Oh, Steven."

"Why didn't you walk home, Steven?"

"You're killing us, Steven."

Steven smiled sheepishly. "Sorry, folks. It's that garbage plate I ate. I guess I shouldnta gone back for that second helping of beans."

"Could this day possibly get any worse?" said Mrs. Levine to no one in particular. A few minutes later she sighed, "There is a God," as the bus pulled off of Goodman Street and into the #27 School parking lot.

Mrs. Levine stood to warn the students to leave the bus in an orderly fashion, but she was almost knocked over by kids stampeding out the door. The last person to exit the bus was Steven who slouched on out, leaving a cloud of noxious fumes trailing behind him.

Chapter 18

Following a discussion between Mrs. Levine, Principal Coley and Mr. Washburn, it was determined that Janie's punishment would be a three day suspension for disobeying a direct order not to bring Princess to Highland Park. None of the adults bought her explanation of innocence by reason that Princess was technically in Jeanetta's book bag. And, she was to spend part of that suspended time writing letters of apology to Mayor Johnson, Mr. Barnes, and the Lilac Festival Committee. Princess was banned from school indefinitely. Mr. Washburn toyed with the idea of making Janie give Princess away, but decided that would be too cruel. Janie had no mother and no sisters or brothers. She needed somebody besides him to love.

Life in the classroom returned to normal—reading, math, spelling, social studies, science, etc. etc. The best part of every day now was the increasingly frequent messages from Granny Rob. Her latest one read:

Subj: Skunks
Date: May 17, 2000

From: Grannyrob@sunnyhill.org
To: Levine217@27susanbee.edu

Hi gang,

I loved hearing about your escapades at Highland Park, and thanks for sending the newspaper article by snail mail. I showed it to Mr. Peters, and we both laughed until we cried. By the way, you wouldn't have any more of that White Lilacs perfume would you? Mr. Peters says that when I'm wearing it I smell just like springtime. Tell Janie to take good care of Princess.

Love from Granny Rob

Mrs. Levine's class responded by having another collection for perfume money. They decided to give up their ice cream money for a few days until they had enough for a big bottle of White Lilacs. Mrs. Levine contributed $3.50. She said that her idea of ice cream was a hot fudge sundae and that's how much they cost. Jeanetta wrote back to Granny Rob. She was still mad at Janie and wanted to tell Granny Rob about it.

Subj: Best friends
Date: May 20, 2000
From: Levine217@27susanbee.edu
To: Grannyrob@sunnyhill.org

Hi Granny Rob,

This is from Jeanetta. Watch your snail mail for a package from Room 217. Here's a hint—it's something that

Mr. Peters will like. Did you ever have a best friend? Janie's my ex-best friend, and I told her that I don't want to talk to her ever again and I don't—except that sometimes I do. Debra wants to be my new best friend, but she doesn't make me laugh the way Janie does, and she doesn't understand that I have to take my sandwiches apart and first eat one side and then the other. And Debra hates red licorice. What should I do?

Love from Jeanetta

After the three-day suspension, Janie was allowed to return to school and the feud was still on. Jeanetta rode in the front of the bus to school. Janie rode in the back. Jeanetta ate lunch with Debra. Janie sat by herself. Jeanetta jumped rope with the other girls at recess. Janie played soccer with the boys. In the classroom they spoke when they absolutely had to, but Janie no longer had Jeanetta to rely on when she couldn't do a math problem. She had to resort to asking Lamar, and asking Lamar wasn't much better than doing it herself.

Meanwhile Granny Rob responded to Jeanetta and to the whole class.

Subj: Best friends
Date: May 24, 2000
From: Grannyrob@sunnyhill.org
To: Levine217@27susanbee.edu

Dear Friends,
    I thank you so much for the new bottle of While Lilacs

perfume. I put some on right away. Then Mr. Peters asked me to go for a stroll with him around the gardens. The gardens here at Sunny Hill are nice—ornamental cherry trees, rhododendrons, and tulips—but not one lilac bush. Mr. Peters said that I smelled better than all of the flowers in the garden. He even held my hand while we sat for a spell on one of those wrought iron benches. I was so surprised you could have knocked me over with a feather. What do you think I should do now?

Personal to Jeanetta:

Yes, Jeanetta, I had a best friend. Her name was Elizabeth. She lived right next door to me on Railroad Street when we were growing up. When we were twenty, she married a salesman and moved to Battle Creek. I was maid of honor in her wedding. We kept in touch over the years. She had four children and nine grandchildren and died five years ago when her heart gave out. Not having any brothers and sisters, Elizabeth meant the world to me. I know Janie hurt your feelings, but neither of you has any brothers or sisters, and I think you should make it up with her. I'd give anything to be able to talk to my friend Elizabeth again.

Love from Granny Rob

Chapter 19

Later that day, Lamar, Derrick and Reinaldo were walking home from school together like they usually did. It had recently rained and they were picking up the worms that seemed to ooze out of every crack in the sidewalk.

"Maybe if we get enough worms Steven will take us fishing," said Lamar.

Not having planned ahead, they didn't have a container to put the worms in, and their hands were soon full of those brown, slimy, wriggling creatures.

"Let's put them in our pockets," offered Lamar.

"No, they might crawl out," said Derrick. "Here, put 'm in my lunch box."

"Oooo, that's gross," said Reinaldo. "Your mama will slap you silly if she finds worms in your lunch box."

"She won't know. I'll sneak in and wash it when she's busy with Louis and Richard. She spends all her time with them anyway, and I told her I'm too old for a lunch box. Besides do you have a better idea?"

Even as he spoke, Reinaldo was having a hard time holding onto the worms he had in his hands. He shrugged and emptied his hands into Derrick's lunch box. Lamar did the same and so did Derrick. Then they bent down for more. It wasn't long before they had a box full of worms.

After the boys checked in at their respective houses and got permission from the mothers, they met again at Lamar's. Just as he had predicted, Derrick's mama had been reading a story to Richard and Louis on the couch when he got home. She didn't notice at all when he transferred the worms to a jar from the recycling bin and washed the lunch box. He even dumped a little bleach in for good measure.

It took only a little convincing for Steven to take them fishing. Steven loved to fish, and it was a perfect day. The rain had stopped and the sun was coming out. He just didn't know if he wanted to be seen hanging around with a bunch of eleven year olds.

"We promise we won't get your car dirty," said Lamar. Everyone knew that Steven's black Mustang GT with the 4.3-liter engine and the "baddest" sound system in Rochester was his life.

"We'll even help you wash it when we get back," chimed in Derrick.

That cinched the deal, and they were off. Steven took them to his favorite fishing spot, which was at the bottom of the Empire Blvd hill on a long pier that jutted out into Irondequoit Bay. No one spoke in the car because the loudness of the sound system made conversation impossible.

"What stinks?" said Derrick as they got out of the

car and retrieved their fishing poles and worms from the trunk.

"That seems to be all you're saying these days, Derrick, 'What stinks?'" commented Reinaldo.

"Well, I wouldn't say it if there wasn't so many stupid smelly things around."

"It's just the fish," explained Steven. There're some dead ones over there on that rock.

"Oh, sick."

"You wanted to come fishin' didn't you? Speaking of smells, how's things with Janie 'n Princess. Did Miz Levine let them back in school yet?"

"Janie's back, but not Princess. I don't think we'll ever see her back in school," answered Lamar.

"That's a shame. I like Princess, and I like Janie too. Are her 'n Jeanetta on speaking terms yet?"

"No," said Derrick, "and I'm tired of giving them messages all day. It's 'Derrick, would you tell Janie that her pencil fell on the floor' from Jeanetta or 'Derrick, would you tell Jeanetta that I need to borrow her calculator' from Janie or 'Derrick, would you tell Janie that my calculator's broke.' All day long it's 'Will you tell Jeanetta this' or 'will you tell Janie that.' Those two girls are drivin' me nuts. I tole Miz Levine, but I don't think she cares if they drive me nuts or not. She just sighs and shakes her head."

"That's pitiful, just pitiful," said Steven.

"Hey, I got a fish!" yelled Lamar. It was a six-inch perch. "It's big enough to keep, too. Mama's gonna love me tonight."

They didn't talk much after that. The perch and the bass were biting like crazy, and it didn't take them long to catch enough fish for all three households for dinner.

"Now can this dude pick out a fishin' spot or what?" said Steven.

They vibrated on home the same way they had come, with the sound system set on the "guaranteed to produce deafness" level and the catch of the day in the trunk. It was too late to wash the car when they got home, so they agreed to meet again the next night.

Derrick's mama was thrilled to see the fish he brought home. She gave Derrick a big hug and ran right out back to clean them for dinner, leaving Louis and Richard staring after her. Maybe mama does love me after all, he thought. Now where did those pests go? His little brothers were not hard to find as they were wandering through the house leaving a trail of red juice dripping behind. Mama's not gonna like this, thought Derrick, but that gives me an idea....

Chapter 20

On Thursday the school day began with an e-mail message and a package. The package turned out to be from Mayor Johnson. Enclosed was Steven's gray sweatshirt, all washed and neatly folded, and an enlarged picture of Steven riding in the purple Cadillac. There was also a note.

Dear Mrs. Levine and students,

I received Janie's apology letter and decided to forgive and forget. Besides, my wife thought that Janie had a point about the skunk being my own skunk. Anyway, I threw all those clothes away and am now returning Steven's sweatshirt. I don't know where he lives, so I am sending it to you with this picture. Tell him that if he ever needs a job to come and see me. At least I was right about one thing—this year's Lilac Festival was one that I will never forget. Keep studying hard.

Sincerely,
Mayor Johnson

The e-mail message was from Granny Rob of course.

Subj: The kiss
Date: May 27, 2000
From: Grannyrob@sunnyhill.org
To: Levine217@27susanbee.edu

Hello Friends,

You won't believe what happened yesterday. We had an ice cream social here at Sunny Hill, and Mr. Peters asked me to go with him. When we were in the elevator to go back upstairs to our floor, he grabbed me and gave me a big kiss—right on the mouth. I kissed him back, and we missed our floor. We had to ride all the way up to six and then back down to two. Have you ever heard of such foolishness? Of course, I was wearing my White Lilacs perfume. I'm telling you it puts some kind of a spell on men—at least on my Mr. Peters.

Janie and Jeanetta, have you two patched up your quarrel yet? It's not right for best friends to fight like this.

Learn a lot today, children.

Love from Granny Rob

Janie read the e-mail message and decided to try one more time to get Jeanetta to talk to her. She started walking towards Jeanetta's desk. But when Jeanetta saw Janie coming, she immediately jumped up and started heading toward the bathroom. Unfortunately, she was in such a hurry that she stepped right on

Derrick's foot that was sticking out into the aisle.

"Ow! Ow! Ow!" yelled Derrick as he grabbed the injured foot.

"Sorry," mumbled Jeanetta as she sped away.

"You shouldn't have your feet sticking out into the aisle, Derrick. If you had been sitting up straight this wouldn't have happened," said Mrs. Levine and she was off on another lecture about keeping their bodies under control.

Great, thought Derrick. Mrs. Levine gets another $100 for this lecture and I get a sore foot. This war between Janie and Jeanetta has got to stop.

***

Later that day the boys met at the Greens' house to help Steven wash his car as they had promised. Steven washed the top himself because he was the only one tall enough to reach it, but he spent the rest of his time ordering his lackeys about.

"There's still a spot on that bumper, Lamar. That there tire rim doesn't shine like it oughtta, Reinaldo. Derrick, you gotta rub harder, man. You ain't gunna get no dirt off like that."

Derrick thought he was back in school. "Pretty soon he'll be giving us a lecture about how a clean car means a clean mind," he whispered to Lamar.

"All this work is making me hungry," complained Reinaldo. "Steven, will you take us down to the Mini-Mart where you work when we get done? I need some potato chips or at least a candy bar."

Then Derrick remembered his plan. "Yeah, Steven, can you take us to the Mini-Mart?" He filled the boys in on his idea and they all agreed to help.

Chapter 21

On Saturday morning Janie, only half awake and followed by Princess, slowly made her way down the front stairs. She was on her way to retrieve the morning newspaper for her dad. Since the incident at Highland Park she had been doing everything she could think of to keep him happy. She opened the front door, and with only one eye open, reached her hand out to grope for the paper. She almost missed seeing the red line that led from her door down the front steps and out onto the sidewalk.

"What is this?" she said out loud. It looks like red licorice." Now she opened both eyes and edged out the door.

"It is red licorice," she said as she bent over to smell it.

Janie was enthralled. Red licorice was her favorite food. She looked down the street. The red licorice seemed to go all the way to the corner. She started following the trail, picking up the licorice as she went along.

***

On that same Saturday morning, Jeanetta and her

mom were getting ready to take the bus downtown.

"Look down the street, Jeanetta and see if you see the bus coming," said Ms. Jones, who was running a little late. Luckily the bus stop was only one block from their house. Jeanetta opened the side door and walked to the sidewalk. Then she looked up the street. She didn't see the bus, but she did see a skinny red line with little bumps going up the street. She looked harder. The skinny line was really red shoestring licorice, and the little bumps were knots that tied it together.

Who would put red licorice on the sidewalk, thought Jeanetta. She forgot all about her mother and the bus as she started picking up the licorice and following the trail. Everyone knew she couldn't pass up red licorice.

***

Janie followed the licorice all the way down Arbutus Street. She wound the licorice around her waist when it got to be too much to hold in her hand. She stopped every few minutes to make sure that Princess was still with her. Sure enough, the loyal Princess was waddling right behind.

***

Jeanetta followed the licorice trail five blocks down Clifford Avenue. It looked like the trail was going to end at Jerold Street, but when she got there, she found that it just turned the corner. Jeanetta was dressed up to go downtown in a gauzy pink and blue flowered dress that went all the way down to her ankles. She didn't want to get her clothes dirty so she started wrapping the licorice around her head when it got to be too much to carry. Jeanetta turned left at Jerold Street and kept on walking.

***

Janie and Princess followed the licorice trail around the corner onto Fernwood Avenue. They kept on walking.

***

Jeanetta kept walking down Jerold Street. The trail seemed to end up ahead or did it just turn again?

***

"Another corner coming up," said Janie to Princess. "How far does this trail go?"

***

Jeanetta moved closer to the corner, her eyes focused on the red line on the ground.

***

Janie moved closer to the corner, her eyes focused on the red line on the ground.

"Eeeeeeek!" yelled Jeanetta when she crashed head first into her former best friend.

"Eeeeeeek!" yelled Janie when their foreheads met in a loud clunk.

Upon impact both girls fell crashing to the ground, and their screams turned to laughter as they took a good look at each other. Janie was still in her pajamas and slippers, but she looked a little like Santa Claus with her big red licorice belly. The licorice around Jeanetta's head looked like a turban, and Janie started calling her Maharani Jones. Meanwhile Princess stood nearby moving those front paws back and forth at a furious rate.

"Are you sure that's really Princess?" teased Jeanetta when they finally stopped laughing.

"I'm sure," said Janie as she reached over to pick Princess up. "Here, Jeanetta, why don't you hold her? I've been thinking, why don't you give Princess a middle name and then you'd be like her godmother."

"You mean it?"

"Yeah. Princess needs a godmother, and I need my best friend back."

Chapter 22

Anyone passing by the corner of Fernwood Avenue and Jerold Street that morning got quite an eyeful. Some people in cars were pointing fingers. Others were looking, blinking their eyes, and then looking again. What they saw was a black girl wearing a red turban sitting next to a white girl in her pajamas holding a skunk in between them. The girls and the skunk were all munching on some strings of red licorice.

That was where their parents found them a few minutes later. It hadn't taken long for Ms. Jones to miss Jeanetta, nor for Mr. Washburn to miss Janie, so both parents were trailing not too far behind their daughters.

"You're not really eating that licorice that's been on the ground?" said Ms. Jones in disgust when she had sized up the situation.

"But Ms. Jones we blew the germs off first," protested Janie sincerely.

"Jackie, why don't you and Jeanetta come back to our house and we'll discuss this over some coffee and jelly doughnuts?" offered Janie's dad.

"That sounds good," replied Jeanetta's mom. "We

missed the bus downtown anyway, and I just know you don't want Janie wandering around the neighborhood in her pajamas."

"Jeanetta, I'll let you carry Princess home," said Janie, "but first truce me that we are best friends again." Janie put up her index and middle fingers together. Jeanetta put up her index and middle fingers together. They linked fingers and said at the same time, "friends forever."

They were almost back to Arbutus Street when they heard the noise. "That's got to be Steven's car," said Jeanetta. "I'd recognize that noise anywhere." Sure enough, Steven and his three disciples were cruising by on their way to another fishing expedition. They had detoured down Fernwood Avenue to see if Derrick's plan had worked.

"Are you boys responsible for littering our sidewalks with all this red licorice stuff?" asked Mr. Washburn in his stern father's voice when they had pulled over to the side of the road.

"It was Derrick's idea," said Reinaldo who was ready to betray his best friend at a moment's notice.

"Well, let me shake your hand, Derrick. You seem to have been able to pull off what none of the rest of us has been able to do. Janie and Jeanetta are finally friends again. Follow us home and come in for some donuts and coffee, er, I mean milk."

Derrick shot an "I told you so" grin at Reinaldo and said, "It wasn't nuthin', Mr. Washburn. I was just tired of passing messages and getting my feet stomped on. But we wouldn't mind some donuts would we boys?"

"S'long as you don't get no powdered sugar or no sticky hands in my car," said Steven. They all proceeded to the Washburn's kitchen where the boys revealed in detail just how many stores they had to visit to buy enough licorice and how long it took them to tie all of those pieces of licorice together.

***

So life in northeast Rochester returned to normal. Well, almost normal. Derrick just couldn't bring himself to use his lunch box for the rest of the year, and his mother never did figure out how the lunch box had gotten to smell like Clorox.

Mrs. Levine and the rest of the students were happy to hear that the feud between Janie and Jeanetta was over. When Mrs. Levine heard that Derrick had been the peacemaker, she nearly fainted in surprise. "Derrick, you never cease to amaze me. I feel like giving you a big kiss."

"That's okay," said Derrick backing away.

"Speaking of kisses," continued his teacher, "there was a new e-mail waiting for me this morning and I copied it for you all to read together."

"What's matrimony, Mrs. Levine?" asked Lamar as he started reading the copies she had passed out.

"Keep reading and you'll find out," she replied.

Subj: Matrimony
Date: June 2, 2000

From: Grannyrob@sunnyhill.org
To: Levine217@27susanbee.edu

My Dear Friends,

Hold onto your hats. Have I got news for you! This old broad is getting married—that's right—married. Mr. Peters proposed and I accepted, and the wedding's a week from Saturday. What do you think about that? Mr. Peters says that at our age we can't afford to wait. My honeybunch is so cute. He had Dr. Howard go out and buy me a ring with a real diamond in it. Of course, I had a little bit of trouble getting it over this arthritic finger of mine, and when Mr. Peters got down on one knee to propose, he had to have the aides help him back up. But other than that, I feel like a teenager again. I wish you all could come to the wedding, but I'll send you a videotape.

Love from Granny Rob soon to be Granny Peters

"Can I be the one to answer Granny Rob's e-mail?" asked Jeanetta. "I want to be the one to tell her that Janie and I are best friends again." Mrs. Levine consented and the rest of the class agreed. Jeanetta wrote:

Subj: Best Friends
Date: June 2, 2000
From: Levine217@27susanbee.edu
To: Grannyrob@sunnyhill.org

Dear Granny Rob,

You told us your good news, and I want to tell you our

good news. Janie and I are best friends again, and it's all thanks to Derrick and some red licorice. Janie's even going to let me be Princess' Godmother.

We can't wait to see the tape of your wedding. What are you going to wear? Will you still e-mail us after you're married? Where are you going on your honeymoon? What are you going to call Mr. Peters after you are married?

Love from Jeanetta and friends

Chapter 23

Jeanetta chose Elizabeth to be Princess' middle name in honor of Granny Rob's best friend named Elizabeth. On Saturday, June 3, 2000 at 10 o'clock in the morning, Jeanetta officially became Princess Elizabeth Washburn's godmother at a special outdoor ceremony. The birdbath in Mrs. Brady's yard next door was chosen as a baptismal font, and the rain that had collected there served as holy water. Derrick, Lamar, and Reinaldo were the witnesses. Steven had been invited too, but he said he didn't get up that early unless he was going fishing.

"This means you have to take care of Princess if I die, you know," said Janie.

"I know," said Jeanetta. "I'll treat Princess like my very own baby." Both girls held up two fingers and truced.

"This is making me sick," said Derrick.

"When do we eat?" said Reindaldo. "You did say we were going to eat didn't you?"

"Yeah, yeah," said Janie. She led the group through the back door and into the kitchen where Mr. Washburn, wearing an apron, was fixing scrambled eggs and pancakes.

Lamar hung back a minute to talk to Jeanetta. "You'll make a great godmother for Princess, Jeanetta. And I'm glad you're back to being best friends with Janie."

"Thanks, Lamar." Jeanetta smiled. This day was just getting better and better.

***

Granny Rob kept her word, and the wedding videotape arrived the last week of school. Mrs. Levine asked them to dress up for the viewing on Thursday, the last day of school, so that they could pretend that they were actual wedding guests. She also baked and decorated a small cake and fixed a Hawaiian Punch and ginger ale concoction so that afterwards they could have a real wedding reception.

The video opened with Granny Rob addressing the camera. "Hello boys and girls at #27 School in Rochester, New York. I'm having this videotape made just for you because I feel like you're my family, the only family I've got. Oh, how I wish you could be here today. Did you know that a bride has to wear:

> something old,
> something new,
> something borrowed,
> something blue?

That's an old rhyme, but I'm an old person so I thought I better stick with it just for good luck. Let me show you what I have.

Well, the something old is easy—that's my Bible (she held it up to the camera) that my grandma read to me out of when I was a little girl.

The something new is this pearl headband (she pointed to a silver and pearl strip on her head.) Sue Ellen put it in when she fixed my hair this morning. It goes good with my gray hair don't you think?

The something borrowed is this pearl necklace (she touched the beautiful chain around her neck) that Dr. Howard's wife loaned me just for today.

And now for the something blue. I probably shouldn't show you this, but a girl like me only gets married once. (She lifted up one side of the long white lace dress she was wearing. There, above the varicose veins and knobby knee, was a blue garter.)

Now let's get the show on the road. I've been waiting 82 years for this. I don't think I can wait any longer."

The camera panned back to show a man dressed in a black suit and wearing a cross. He was standing in front of Granny Rob and Mr. Peters, who were sitting close together and holding hands. She was wearing a corsage of pink roses and white baby's breath. A young (fiftyish) woman was playing "True Love" on the piano while the guests with canes tapped them to the music. The guests in wheel chairs just sang or hummed along.

What followed was a short, but beautiful, wedding ceremony. When the preacher asked Mr. Peters if he would take Brenda Robinson for his lawfully wedded wife, he said, "You betcha." When he asked Miss

old

new

borrowed

blue

Robinson if she would take Charles Peters for her lawfully wedded husband, she said, "Yes, indeed."

"I now pronounce you man and wife," said the preacher.

The video went on to show the wedding cake and the rest of the party.

After a few minutes Granny Rob came back on and addressed the camera. "Boys and girls, I hope you liked the wedding. I don't want to leave without answering some of your questions. Of course I'll still e-mail you, but you can call me Granny Pete now. I waited all these years to get married, and I want to use my husband's name. I think I'll still call Mr. Peters, Mr. Peters— except when I call him honeybunch of course. As for the honeymoon, the staff here at Sunny Hill offered to take us to the Dairy Queen for a sundae. I think I'll even ask for whipped cream and a cherry. I guess you can see for yourselves here what I'm wearing so I won't describe my dress. But even though I've got on these pink roses, you know that behind my ears I've sprayed lots of White Lilacs." She winked into the camera.

"You never know what a little White Lilacs can do."

Author's Note

Home to over 1200 lilac bushes and hundreds of other flowers and trees, Rochester's Highland Park is an arboretum designed by Frederick Law Olmsted, who also helped design New York City's Central Park. Designed to look entirely natural, Highland Park was actually planted with many rare trees. A number of the lilacs were bred there. Highland Park is one of three Rochester parks designed by Olmsted. The others are Genesee Valley Park and Seneca Park, both of which are found along the Genesee River. Rochester, NY is one of only four cities in the country that have a whole park system designed by Olmsted.

The Lilac Festival is a 10-day event held every May in Highland Park. It is Rochester's oldest and most anticipated annual festival. Although the spring celebration now includes food, musical entertainment, a parade, a 10K race, children's activities, and arts and crafts, the lilacs and their sweet scent are still the stars of the show. In 2006 the lilac was named the official state bush of New York State. More information about Highland Park and this year's Lilac Festival can be found at:

www.lilacfestival.com
www.monroecounty.gov/parks-highland.php
www.libraryweb.org/rochimag/lilacs/home.htm

Although the Lilac Festival is a real celebration held in Rochester every year, all of the events and characters in this book are fiction except for Mayor William A. Johnson, Jr., Rochester's mayor from 1994–2006. However, Mayor Johnson has never been sprayed by a skunk. Skunks are wild creatures that may carry rabies. They should NOT be made into pets.

Thanks to Tim O'Connell, tour guide extraordinaire, for correcting my historical facts and to Zach Steffen and Pyramid Publishing for helping me put all of this together.

About the Author

Sally Valentine is a native Rochesterian who has been both a student and a teacher in the Rochester City School District. After teaching math for twenty-five years, she is now off on a tangent of writing. *What Stinks?* is the third book in a series of novels she is writing about the people and places of Rochester. The first two books, *The Ghost of the Charlotte Lighthouse* and *Theft at George Eastman House*, are part of the North Country Books New York State Adventure series. Check out her website at www.RochesterAuthor.com. Teachers who would like to use the books as part of their Social Studies curriculum may download free worksheets for each book, and you may contact her there for school visits. Sally is currently working on her next novel, *Lost at Sea Breeze*, and also a book of poems for children about places in New York State entitled, *There are no Buffalo in Buffalo*.

THE WATER OF LIFE REMAINS IN THE DEAD

Maria Nieto

FLORICANTO PRESS

FLORICANTO™ PRESS

7177 Walnut Canyon Rd.

Moorpark, California 93021

(415) 793-2662

www. FLORICANTOPRESS. com

ISBN-13: 9781888205596

Cover Art *The Grieving: Ciudad Juárez 2004* by Rebekah Tarín (brushfireartemasfina.com, brushfire575@gmail.com)

"*Por nuestra cultura hablarán nuestros libros. Our books shall speak for our culture.*"

Roberto Cabello-Argandoña, Editor

WATER OF LIFE

ACKNOWLEDGMENTS

I am honored that the talented artist, Rebekah Tarín, gave permission to use the image of her painting entitled, *The Grieving: Ciudad Juarez 2004*, for the book's cover. As I have worked to do with this story, Rebekah's art forces us to see the unseen; the victims we never knew, those killed under the cover of nightfall. The adventures of Alejandra Marisol, the protagonist in this story, came to life with the support of so many. I am grateful to my mom, Caroline Aguirre, Rebecca Carrillo, Irma Castruita, Helen Garfinkle, Electra Flink, Jane Armbruster, Karen Choury, and my aunts, Helen (Varmint) Nájera and Virginia Andrade, for their willingness to read an early draft of the work. Their feedback was instrumental to keep me in the writing trenches when the negative voices tried to drag down my spirit. Gratitude goes out to Terry Cunningham, Jane Barbarow, and Lucha Corpi, who provided detailed edits following multiple readings of the work. They were tough, pushing me to let go of text that was strangling the pace of the story. The quality of the wording and storyline were vastly improved with their input and I am indebted for their generous gift of time and commitment. I am deeply thankful to former LAPD detective (Robbery-Homicide Division), William Williams. William's knowledge of LAPD procedures and tactics, in addition to his expertise in American history, proved invaluable in the research phases of this work. I would also like to thank Jennifer Brody for allowing me to share a personal memory that I used in this book. Over the course of three years to write this story, Jennifer Vásquez was there to listen to half-baked ideas, offer advice, and provide loving, daily support. I am lucky and thankful to be on this journey with her. Finally, I thank my publisher at Floricanto Press, Roberto Cabello-Argandoña, and editor, Leyla Namazie, for their commitment to Latino stories and voices.

Chapter 1

NO BED OF ROSES

Hell did not encircle a wretched pit beneath layers of molten earth. No, from where I stood, it was located in East Los Angeles at the southern edge of Belvedere Park. There I could see the outline of the devil's playground; five murdered men whose bodies showed the signs of Detective Ashworth's sadistic handiwork. How was it possible? I had seen Ashworth writhe in pain and take his last breath. He had confessed to everything before swallowing the cyanide capsule, and from all accounts these latest murders occurred after his death.

I felt a tug at my arm. "This is a restricted area, Miss. You'll need to leave."

"My name is Alejandra Marisol. I'm a reporter for the *Los Angeles Times.*"

"Leave her be, Deputy." I turned to find Lieutenant Smitz towering over me. He no longer intimidated me unlike the first time we met. I had gone to see the high ranked sheriff to inquire about two unsolved murders. Days later I learned the victims died at the hands of John Ashworth.

"Miss Marisol, I didn't think you'd want to see me again," He said with a sarcastic tone.

"Seems that bourbon, or is it the Scotch you drink each night is pickling your brain."

"What gave you the idea I might have a drink from time to time?"

"It's all over your face. And the liquor lines tell me from time to time, really means all of the time with you."

"Ah, a little spitfire. What's it been, a week since we first met? You've grown some backbone."

"One doesn't almost get killed, not once but several times, witness unspeakable horrors, and not get affected by it."

"Seems you'd understand my indulgences then, which by the way, favor the taste of Tennessee Whiskey, straight up, no rocks."

"Drinking, okay, I get it. You have a tough job. But I'll never understand your penchant to hurt me, and others like me, all out of pure contempt. You're a racist bigot, plain and simple."

"What makes you think you can talk to me like that and still get what you want, a closer look at the crime scene for your story?"

I took a breath. I had never felt so strong and in control. "Look, I'm tied to this hell, which I thought ended when Detective Ashworth died and his Los Angeles Police Department accomplices were arrested. But now there's a truck with five bodies, and it's going to catch headlines. People will want answers."

"Ashworth was LAPD, my department wasn't involved."

"Right. Your Sheriff's Department is above the fray for now. If the investigation determines these murders are tied to a child sex trade operation and that one of your kind orchestrated it, the public won't care if it's a Sheriff or an LAPD cop who's to blame."

Smitz turned away. He drew his right hand up to his forehead and slowly pulled his hand across and down his crew cut hairline. He turned back toward me and I could see the look of surrender in his face. He motioned for me to follow as he led the way toward a bloodstained white pickup truck.

There was no sanity in what I saw. Each man had been butchered. Slaughtered was the right word. Their eyes stared at me, begging me to know their slow and painful death.

In a voice wrenched with defeat Smitz spoke, "It's a horror show."

Smitz's words didn't even begin to tell the story. Some say the moment we die our soul is unchained and the pain of life that dug its claws into our flesh ceases. Suffering ends, furrows fade, and the face of youth reappears. I saw no such face among these men. I saw a fate no one should come to know. I focused on one man; he was young. Like the other victims he had been skinned with an arm torn off. His eyes bulged. His mouth locked open. I could imagine his screams; a relentless torment that raged until he was freed from this world. I kept my eyes on him, hoping my stare could change the scene or make it go away. The pungent odor of oxidized iron from the pools and spatter of blood covering the truck's bed confirmed I couldn't change a thing.

I turned away from the grisly scene. "Who will be the detective on the case?"

"Leighton Carr. I'll introduce you."

10

Smitz called out to Carr who stood at the front end of the truck jotting notes. "Detective Carr."

Carr was short and stout, and the grey suit jacket reaching down to his knees made him appear compressed. "Smitz, you old man. Why the formality?"

"There's someone I want you to meet. This is Alejandra Marisol. I think you'll find her a good resource for your case."

Detective Carr gave me a sideways glance and directed his attention to Smitz. "So tell me how this woman is going to help?"

"There's a good chance these bodies are tied to Detective Ashworth out of LAPD, the one who took his life the other night. Alejandra was working with him, investigating a sex ring. She didn't know Ashworth ran the sick operation, but in the end she was the one who brought him down."

"So you're telling me Miss Marisol was duped by Ashworth and happened to be lucky enough to get out of a pretty dangerous spot. There's no way she's going to be part of this investigation, no way in hell. Anyway, I'm steps ahead of her. Just saw Ashworth's body at the morgue and after I leave here I'm heading to his house."

"I know what you're thinking Carr, I thought the same thing, but the girl's got fire in her belly. Why limit your resources? She may have insights into Ashworth that can help with the case."

I cut in, "Ashworth wasn't just operating a sex ring; it was a child sex trade and I was deep into the investigation."

Carr questioned, "Investigation? Where do you work?"

"I'm a reporter with the *Times*."

"Oh no, Smitz. You can't be serious. You want me to work with a reporter?"

"She's got info on this case that hasn't even been penned to a report. She knows stuff."

"But I can't officially let her take part in this investigation. You know that."

I answered for Smitz. "Unofficially, you can. Look, you're going to Ashworth's home, let me go with you."

An exasperated Carr responded. "Damn it, woman, you're not going."

Smitz complied, "Okay, Carr has the final word on

this. I won't pull rank. Homicide detectives call the shots on the murders."

Carr smirked in my direction. He turned and walked away.

My jaw clamped and I could feel the heat rise in my face, but I stayed calm. One way or another I'd get inside Ashworth's house.

Chapter 2

HOUSE CALL

I had what I needed for my assignment. I could return to the *Times* Building, write the initial report on these murders, and end my part in it. But my gut told me the macabre scene was tied to someone other than Ashworth. Someone who wanted to send a message: a warning that a cruel and painful death awaited me or anyone else who wanted to dig for the truth. The danger signs were clearly posted, but I didn't care. I was ready for battle.

I sat in *Azulita*, my blue VW Beetle, and stared in the rearview mirror at my blank canvas, a pair of pale bow shaped lips. I grabbed my war paint: a tube of Revlon lipstick color number 703. "Brazen Bliss," the cosmetic company's top selling color for women with caramel brown skin like mine was my talisman of late; it unleashed a fire inside. With the precision of a portrait painter I set to work. I started at one end by applying subtle pressure as I spread the rich red and tawny tones across my bottom lip to the opposite corner of my mouth. I then used the tip of my tool to outline the top of my canvas before filling it in with color.

Waiting for Carr to finish his work at the crime scene, I knew I needed to summon all the strength, imagined or real I could get.

I kept my eyes on Carr and watched as he got into his dark brown sedan and drove off. I followed him into Pasadena as he wound his way up Lake Avenue beneath the shadow of Echo Mountain to turn down a tree-lined street in Altadena. Carr stopped behind a patrol car parked in the driveway of a nondescript single level home. I kept my distance and pulled against the curb three houses away.

In less than an hour, Carr and two patrol deputies left. I made my way down a long driveway to the rear of the house. I tried my luck with the sliding glass patio door, but no go; it was locked. I noticed the other side of the house was out of public view, shielded by a high concrete wall and an overgrown oleander bush. After pushing through the shrubbery, I found a small bathroom window ajar. With my hands pressed against the house and legs pushed up against the back wall, I inched upward. I strained to hold position and used my right hand to push the window open. I propelled forward and nearly landed head first into the toilet bowl as I hit the ground.

Sore from the impact I moved slowly to stand. The

bathroom was unremarkable. A single towel hung over a hook on the wall and the standard items sat on a shelf above the sink: shaving cream, razor, and cologne.

Ashworth's bedroom was my next stop. There I found a scene of meticulous order. A lone chest of drawers alongside a bed that could easily pass a drill sergeant's inspection sat centered against one wall. I opened each drawer to find perfect rows of t-shirts, socks and underwear, all folded as if on display at a high-end department store. Ashworth's closet mirrored the same attention to detail. Jackets and slacks were neatly hung and organized by color. Shoes were aligned on the floor and fitted with shoehorns.

I walked to the living room where a drab beige chair and sofa sat against an eggshell painted wall. The only color in the room came from a lone painting of a small boat tied alongside a riverbank. The place reminded me of a hospital waiting room. I turned to find a small desk and chair at the other end of the room. A framed photograph sat on the desk; the only personal effect in the entire house. It pictured Ashworth standing with an attractive woman and two small children. I presumed the woman was one of his ex-wives. Everyone in the picture smiled; they looked happy. The image of Ashworth was in sharp contrast to the psychopath I came to know: a cold and calculating killer.

I searched the rest of the house and came up empty. Maybe Carr had found something and taken it with him? I had my doubts. I looked back at the photo with Ashworth. "What are you still hiding, you madman?"

The photo didn't fit the space. I was curious to see if there was a year written on it. I removed the frame's backing and there behind the picture were the names John, Shirley, Katie and John Jr. with the year 1960 written underneath. As I replaced the happy family portrait in the frame the cardboard insert slipped and three weathered Polaroid photos fell free. In the first one, I immediately identified a younger Ashworth dressed in his LAPD patrol uniform. He was standing with other officers whom I recognized as well. They were the same men, his child sex trade accomplices, who had tried to kill us. But one man in the picture, also dressed in his LAPD "blues", I didn't recognize.

The next photograph pictured an older man with a look of shock running across his face as the camera caught him in bed with a much younger woman. I moved to the last photo. It pictured a younger man with a naked woman tied to the bed. The woman's head was turned to the side; her eyes avoided the camera's lens. The man on top of her looked smug and angry.

I wondered if these photos represented Ashworth's start in photography before he began taking pictures of the kids he intended to sell for sex. In comparison to Ashworth's work using younger subjects these photos were benign. Nevertheless, I wanted to find out if they were somehow tied to the five murdered men.

Chapter 3

MAKING BONES ABOUT IT

Even though I had met him less than a week ago, my heart pumped at full speed for Dr. Armand Gomez. I felt no need to put on the brakes. I was ready to enjoy the ride wherever it took me. Armand's call rocked me out of bed, and in a matter of minutes I dressed and left to meet him at the morgue. He had worked through the night conducting autopsies on the five dead men.

When I arrived I found Armand placing a heart in a large open scale. "Alejandra, good to see you. Let me get the weight on this and I'll be right with you. They just brought this guy in about an hour ago. Looks like he died of a heart attack in his sleep, but since he was found on the street he became a coroner's case."

"The work never ends for you, does it?"

"You're right, death is the one thing I count on, or rather counts on me, everyday."

Armand removed his gloves and moved in closer. "I'd sure like to count on something else."

He raised his hand to my face and gently brushed my cheek. In one smooth, uninterrupted move he placed his head into the crook of my neck. I felt his long curls as he paused to breathe in my smell. I wanted nothing more than to feel his full lips on my skin. "You've got me spinning, Alejandra. I'd love to be able to count on seeing you."

I could barely say the words. "I'd like that."

"You just made my day. Now, I guess we should focus on those victims for you. Come on over, I think you'll be pleased with what I have so far."

Armand grabbed his notes. "First, looks like the victims spent some time in cold storage after they were killed so I can't give you an exact time of death."

"But from what I saw it seemed as if all five men were massacred in the bed of the truck. It didn't look like the bodies had been moved there."

"Detective Carr had the same idea. He thinks maybe someone drove the truck into some sort of cold storage warehouse."

"Armand, they must have been stored close by. Who would risk driving through the streets of L.A. with bloodied bodies in the back of a truck?"

Armand concurred. "You've got a point."

"Since the bodies were in cold storage that means Ashworth could have killed them before he died."

"I wouldn't be able to rule out that possibility."

"What else do you have?"

"All of the men bled to death after their arms were torn off. There were no tattoos or scars, which may have told us something about their identity. One of the men, approximate age 55, showed lung damage; the air sacs were inflamed and there was scar tissue. I'm running some tests to see if I can tell what caused it. The other four men appear to be much younger. I'd say about 20 years of age."

"How did you figure out the ages?"

"I look at the ribs of the sternum. The integrity at the end of a rib can tell you a lot."

"That's amazing, but I wish we had names."

"I might have a partial name for the older victim. ED, maybe short for Eduardo, is stamped into the victim's leather belt. After I found small pieces of leather under the victim's index fingernail I re-examined the belt. Not sure what it means, but it looks like the victim etched five numbers into the leather. Maybe he was trying to leave a clue knowing he was about to die."

"Can I take a look?"

"Sure, here it is. The numbers follow his name."

I questioned, "But what could five numbers mean? You need seven for a phone number. Could it be part of an address?"

"I don't know, but there's more. Although the left arm on the body has been removed, I'm certain the hands from both arms were tied pretty tight at one point. Look here, below the wrist. Bruising and lacerations indicate he must have been bound with a coarse rope. The deepest laceration is on the radius side of the arm. It indicates the victim made an effort to etch the numbers in such a way they'd follow his name on the side of the belt. Not sure why he didn't just etch the numbers, where he'd have greatest access and ease, on the stretch of leather running across his back."

"Looks as if he may have been interrupted too. Even though I can tell this last number is a three, it's not complete. I'm guessing if he had more time he would have etched in a full phone number."

Armand responded with anticipation in his voice. "I

think we'll know more after my cousin, Olivia, runs some tests."

"Olivia?"

"She's a biochemist, a real genius. She's always inventing something in her laboratory at Caltech. I tell her about my cases and sometimes she can help. She'll be here any minute to pick up some samples."

"What kind of samples?"

"Teeth and bone. Ah, there she is now."

I turned to see a middle-aged woman with short, wiry gray hair. I immediately saw the family resemblance. Like Armand she had deep dimples bordering the corners of her lips, and her eyes were warm and embracing. With the eagerness and energy of a schoolgirl she greeted Armand.

"¡Hola, Primo! How's my baby cousin? Knee deep in blood today?"

Armand walked over to give his cousin a big hug and then turned toward me. "Olivia, this is Alejandra."

"Good to meet you. I'm happy to see my cousin spending time with a beautiful woman who's still in possession of her soul, unlike the bodies lining the halls in here."

I was immediately taken with Olivia's charm much like the day I met Armand. "Nice to meet you, Olivia. I hear you might be able to shed some light on the case."

"Well I hope so. Armand gives me a chance to put my experimentation to good use, and with the samples he'll give me I should be able to determine where the victims have been living over the last few years and where they were born."

Anxiously I asked, "How can you do that?"

"Science lifts the fog so one can see."

I questioned Olivia again, "But how?"

"We are what we drink, and the water we drink comes from the rain that falls around us. The water molecules in rain contain oxygen, and inside the nucleus of most oxygen atoms there are 16 small sub-atomic particles. Hence, we call it oxygen 16 or write it like this."

Olivia wrote the notation ^{16}O on paper for me to see and then continued. "Oxygen 16 makes up most of the oxygen found in water. Although less abundant in comparison, water also contains other types of oxygen atoms that have more sub-atomic particles and are therefore heavier, like oxygen 18. An easy way to look at it is to see that every glass of water we drink mostly contains oxygen 16, but a bit of oxygen 18 will be there too. Here's where it gets really interesting. The ratio of oxygen 18 to oxygen 16 found in rainwater naturally varies from one geographic location to another."

I piped in, "I think I see where you're going."

"You got it, Honey. I will be able to determine the ratio of oxygen 18 to oxygen 16 in the teeth and bone of each victim. Once I have the ratios I'll compare them to known values for rainwater across geographic areas. Since most teeth are formed by childhood, determining the ratio for this tissue will tell me where the person was born or at least where they spent their early childhood years. On the other hand, because new bone tissue gets made over time, determining the ratio for this sample type will tell me where the person lived over the last few years. So you see, as sure as a rock turns to dust, the water of life remains in the dead."

Armand couldn't contain his pride. "Isn't she brilliant?"

I couldn't hold back either. "This is incredible."

Olivia agreed, "Yes, quite incredible. Armand go ahead and give me the samples and I'll get to work as soon as I get back to the lab."

With the samples in hand Olivia approached me. "It was so nice to meet you. Off I go."

"I'd better go too."

"Not so fast, Alejandra. You're forgetting about Ashworth's body."

"I assumed there'd be nothing to tell me other than what I already knew. He died from cyanide poisoning."

"Did you know about the wolf tattoo on Ashworth's arm?"

Armand's question had recalled an image I would never forget. When I first saw the photo of a man sexually violating a screaming child, I had no idea it was Ashworth. The photo had been ripped and Ashworth's face had been torn away. But the arm with a wolf tattoo, the one he used to restrain a child, was clearly visible. Ashworth had savagely killed people to get that photograph back in his possession, and he had come close to killing me for it, too.

I answered Armand with a cool voice. "I know about it. If there's a devil, then Ashworth is his name. Do me a favor, when you see Detective Carr don't tell him I was here?"

26

"Your secret is safe with me."

"Thanks. Will I see you later?"

Armand responded with a smile. "You can count on it."

When I returned to the morgue reception I recognized the woman in the photograph with Ashworth. It was his ex-wife. She stood with an older man. I slowed to hear her conversation with the receptionist.

"I'm here to claim a body."

"The mortuary should be able to handle that for you, Ma'am."

"Yes, they should be here any minute. I wanted to oversee the process. My daughter asked me to."

"Name of the deceased?"

"John Ashworth."

"Your name?"

"Shirley James."

"Relation?"

"I'm his ex-wife."

"Please have a seat."

The likeness was clear. Shirley James was the woman pictured in the family portrait with Ashworth. Why was she here? The look on her face suggested she wasn't just here for her daughter. Her eyes told me at one time she loved John Ashworth. Maybe she never stopped? How did a vile man get a beautiful woman to love him? Another example of how life makes no sense; no sense at all.

Chapter 4

IT'S ALL IN THE EYES

Large fans set off a collective rattle as their metal caged heads oscillated from side to side; the loud din muted the sound of typing in the newsroom. As expected, Harriett's editorial office rivaled the Los Angeles skyline with its thick layer of hovering haze.

"How can you breathe in here?" I asked.

"Light one up. I guarantee you won't notice the smoke anymore. Plus, after what we just went through barely escaping with our lives; these little babies keep me from losing my last nerve."

In a rare sight Harriett's greying blond hair wasn't snared in a bun. Her thick locks fell onto the shoulders of a tailored pantsuit. She tapped out another cigarette from her pack and lit it using a smoldering butt. "Did you learn anything from the crime scene? I thought I would have heard from you yesterday."

"I guess I expected to see you at Rocky's."

"Right, you live in the same fourplex. Rocky decided to come to my place and make me dinner. Said I needed a good home-cooked meal."

"Yeah, I noticed he didn't make it home last night."

"Keeping tabs on him, eh?"

"Only with the best intentions. He's like my dad."

"Yes, he told me he thinks of you like a daughter." Harriett got right back to business. "So what do you have?"

"As you already know there were five men murdered. None of them had ID. The medical examiner, Armand Gomez, was able to get a rough idea of their ages by examining their ribs. I should know more after Armand's cousin runs some tests. She's a scientist from Caltech and she thinks she'll be able to determine where they were born and where they've been living over the last few years."

"How's that possible?"

"It's a long story, but when Armand gives me the results I'll let you know."

"Armand, huh. First name basis, I see things are going well with the doctor."

"Uh..."

"No need to get flustered, you're not the only one who found love through this hell with Ashworth. Anything else on the murders?"

"The investigating officer on the case, Detective Carr, is not cooperating. I followed him to Ashworth's house though. When he left I managed to make my way inside and found these."

I threw the three photographs onto Harriett's desk.

"What do we have here?"

"Look at the first one. There's Ashworth when he was an LAPD patrol officer. I recognize all of the others with him, except for the one on the end."

Harriett agreed, "Yes, I recognize all of these monsters too. The men who were bent on killing me, all of us. The man on the end, I don't recognize either."

"I need to find out who he is. Any ideas?"

"I have a good contact at LAPD's Internal Affairs Division. If he was LAPD then Captain Allen should be able to help identify him. I'll call the captain before you leave and ask him if he has time to see you."

"That'd be great."

Harriett picked up the next photo. "Damn. This is

Judge Thomas. Ha, I can't say I'm surprised."

"What do you know about him?"

"Important man, a judge for the superior court with aspirations for a seat on the Supreme Court of California. He would have paid dearly to keep this photo from reaching the press."

"I guess I'll have to pay him a visit and ask."

"That's not possible. He died a couple months back. If I remember correctly, it was a heart attack at 90."

"Literally, that's a dead end."

Harriett moved on to the last photo. "Looks like this guy was also caught with his pants down. Don't know who he is, but his eyes strike me as familiar."

"Do you think he could be some sort of public figure?"

"Hell, I don't know, but I'd guess there's a strong possibility since his photo was found with the one of Judge Thomas. I'll bet Judge Thomas and this other man were being blackmailed. Alejandra, do you think we're still in danger? Whoever killed those five men may want to come after us, too."

"I think if they wanted to come after us they would have already done so. I think the five men were killed to tie up loose ends. Killing us would only make a mess of things."

"Did Dr. Gomez, oh, I mean Armand, give you an estimate on time of death?"

"He can't, not exactly. Looks like the bodies spent some time in cold storage."

"Wouldn't that mean Ashworth could be responsible?"

"I'm sure that's what Detective Carr thinks, and he'll use it to close the case."

"And I gather from your response you don't think Ashworth committed these murders."

"I don't. In my gut I know this doesn't end with Ashworth; it only begins with him. Right now, I just need the time to prove it."

"Well, Girl, you're tenacious I'll give you that. I'll support you on my end as long as I can. You won't have a lot of time. Once Carr closes the case there will be pressure on the paper to follow in short order."

"Why?"

"The public won't like the idea that murdering sexual predators are on the loose. The paper will give the public what it wants: a nicely wrapped package tied with a pretty bow."

"Even if that package is carrying lies?"

"I've been around a long time and from my editorial vantage point the public has proven one thing over and over: they love their Pablum. This paper is happy to comply and spoon feed it."

"Well, I don't like Pablum. I prefer a plate of spicy jalapeños. I'll keep you posted on what I turn up."

"Be careful, Alejandra. Oh, and try not to break the law. The police and this paper won't stand idly by if you're caught breaking into someone's house."

"Got it."

Chapter 5

MAN IN BLUE

Captain Allen assured Harriett he could help identify the man in the photograph, assuming he was an LAPD police officer. As the head of the Internal Affairs Division, Harriett told me the captain had access to information on every officer. It didn't take long for me to walk from the *Times* building over to Parker Center; a sleek edifice with an exterior made of glass and white stone on Los Angeles Street. You didn't have to look twice to see how LAPD's administration building earned the nickname "Glass House."

When I arrived at Captain Allen's office on the sixth floor, a cherub faced man dressed in a tailored uniform greeted me with a smile. He reached out both of his hands and I instinctively held out mine to meet him in a warm clasp.

"Welcome, Alejandra. Harriett told me to expect you. Sorry to hear about your awful run in with John Ashworth. Even though I'm coming into this a bit late, I want to do anything I can to help. I wish we could have stopped him before he was able to hurt so many."

"Happy to be here. Any help I can get would be great."

Captain Allen chuckled, "Ha, there aren't many who are happy to be here. Internal Affairs or IAD as we call it isn't a favorite. No matter, I like what I do. It's important to have watchdogs out there. And still some, like Ashworth, get through the cracks."

Captain Allen took a seat and motioned for me to do the same. "You know Alejandra, I can't help but think that many of the problems within our department stem from the days when Chief Parker held the reins. Parker's 'Thin Blue Line' played like a perpetual Disneyland ticket for rogue cops to ride their patrol cars and do as they pleased."

"What's the 'Thin Blue Line'?"

"Parker's strategy to decrease the number of beat officers on the street. And, in their place, increase the number of officers in patrol cars. Parker thought less contact with the public would cut out corruption. Instead, it increased unchecked brutality in certain neighborhoods. I saw it firsthand and I couldn't stand it. When I had the opportunity to leave the streets, I did. That's how I found my way here."

Captain Allen smiled and continued. "How long have you worked with Harriett?"

"Not long, I really just started as a reporter. For the last year I was learning the trade as an intern."

"Well, you're in good hands with Harriett. I love that woman. She's as loyal as they come. Did Harriett tell you how we came to know each other?"

"No."

"I guess she wouldn't. She keeps personal information to herself. About a year after my first wife died from that damn cancer, I met Angie and we eventually got married. I was surprised when she said yes. There aren't many women who'll decide to settle down with a man who has a kid. Ha, I think she fell in love with my little Emily before she fell in love with me."

"How does Harriett fit in?"

"I met Harriett through Angie. They're good friends. Without Harriett's help I could have lost Emily."

"What do you mean?"

"Pam was the name of my first wife. After she died

her family fought me for custody."

"But why would they want to take a daughter away from her father?"

"As you might imagine there's a load of hate in this world and Pam's family added to it. I could never understand how she survived growing up with them. When I married Angie they claimed I was raising my daughter in an unfit home."

"Because you remarried?"

"Because Angie is black. It didn't sit well with Pam's family."

"How did Harriett help?"

"Pam's family ran a huge hog farming operation in Missouri. And to show how small the world can be, Harriett's second cousin owned the adjacent property. Harriett got her cousin to sue the family for the hog stench. Funny thing, no one lived on her cousin's property. Hence, no one had to deal with the smell. All that didn't matter, Pam's family was set to lose a load of money in the suit."

"I smell more than hog stench. Maybe a bit of blackmail?"

"Blackmail is such strong word. In this case I prefer

persuasion. In the end Pam's family backed out of their custody fight, and in exchange Harriett's cousin signed a document stating he would never bring a suit against them for their stench. You got to love it. Their own rotten smell brought them down."

"My Grandmother has a saying, *se puede lavar la suciedad de la piel, pero no la de su alma.* It means you can wash the dirt off your skin but not from your soul."

"I like that. Now, enough about me. Harriett said you have a photograph to show me."

"Yes, here it is. It's of Ashworth. He's standing alongside other cops, his accomplices, who have all been arrested. This cop on the end though, I don't recognize him. I'm hoping you can get a name for me."

Captain Allen smirked. "That's Gary Bell. He was on the force for 19 years before we let him go."

"He was fired?"

"Yep, one too many domestic disputes. His wife Patricia finally filed charges against him for a beating he put her through. Gary was mad as a hornet when he found out he'd be missing a 20 year pension by a couple of months, but my hands were tied."

"Do you have an address for him?"

"I heard his wife took him back. Maybe you can find him at his last known address. Let me check the file."

"Thanks, this really helps."

Captain Allen picked up his phone and dialed an extension. In less than a minute a secretary walked in with Gary Bell's file.

"Ah, here's the address. The place isn't too far from here. Just up the way on Bunker Hill. What do you need from this guy? Are you thinking he was one of Ashworth's accomplices?"

"I never saw him with Ashworth, so I'm guessing he wasn't involved. But since he's in this photo he might know something about Ashworth that can help."

"Alejandra, this guy has a temper. I can go with you."

"I need to do this on my own. I don't want him spooked when I tell him Ashworth is dead, assuming he doesn't already know. Thanks for everything."

§§§§§§§

The address for Gary Bell took me over the second

street tunnel to a weathered apartment building that sloped down a hillside. The only redeeming quality of the place appeared to be its full view of the downtown skyline. I made my way to an outside staircase and followed a corridor that wrapped around the side of the building to apartment #9. The door opened before I could even knock.

My presence surprised the disheveled middle-aged woman who stood in the doorway. "Whoa."

"Patricia?"

"Yeah."

"Sorry to bother you. I'm looking for Gary Bell."

"I got two things to say to you, Sister, that jackass doesn't live here and I'm on my way to work."

"Do you think you can spare a minute so I can ask you a couple of questions? I can walk with you."

The lanky woman brushed me to the side, slammed her front door closed, and locked it. She turned toward me and demanded, "Who's asking?"

"My name is Alejandra Marisol. I'm with the *Times*. I came to ask Gary about his friend, John Ashworth."

"John. He's another jackass. That's all I have to say."

The woman picked up her pace as she trotted down

the stairs. Following close behind I asked, "Do you know where I can find Gary?"

"Hell if I know."

I maneuvered in front of her. "I really need to speak with him."

"Look, I kicked him out close to a year ago. I don't know where he's living."

"Okay, thanks for your time. If you think of anything I can be reached at this number."

I gave her my card and started to walk away disappointed. Then Patricia yelled, "You can try the Olympic Auditorium. That's where he was working security when I kicked him out. If you see that SOB tell him he owes me money."

Chapter 6

MAN OF A THOUSAND MASKS

I opened the door to my unit when *Tía* Carmen called out. "*M'ija,* you're home. You've been gone all day. Come and sit with me."

Living in the same fourplex allowed for unplanned visits. Today, given what I had seen, I wanted to be alone and free to retreat into my shell before trying to find Gary Bell.

I pushed past my need for solitude. "Hey Carmen. I've been working to get some leads on those men who were found murdered in Belvedere Park."

"Horrible, *M'ija*. I can't believe this damn nightmare isn't over."

"The sight I saw, no one should witness. I have a lead though. I need to see if I can find this friend of Ashworth's. He may be working at the Olympic Auditorium."

"Really, M'ija? Are you going over there?"

"I'm going tonight. There will be wrestling at the Auditorium and I'm hoping he'll be there."

"Me and Jaime want to go with you."

"I'll be safe. I just want to talk with this guy."

"*M'ija*, I need to go. I need to think about something else. Okay, *M'ija*?" Carmen looked worried.

"What's going on?" I asked.

"I need to talk to you about something."

I sat close to Carmen on her glider. She grabbed my hands and spoke softly. "Jaime brought me to the doctor today. I didn't want to go, but he made me."

"Made you, why?"

"He noticed some blood oozing from my right breast."

"From where, a cut?"

"No *M'ija*, my nipple."

My heart sank with dread. "*Tía*, how long has this been going on?"

"Oh *M'ija*, I don't know. For a while I think, but I thought it would go away. I didn't want to think about it. I figured the blood was from a *pinche* pimple. After all, nothing ever came out of Te or Ta before, not even a drop of milk from me."

"Te or Ta?"

"I named them, *M'ija*. My left breast is Te and

my right one is Ta. Together that makes *Teta*, you know, Spanish for tit."

Carmen laughed and I couldn't help but do the same. "Oh, Carmen."

"The doctor, he checked me, said they need to do surgery, right away. He told me I'm going to lose a breast, my Ta."

"Does he think you have cancer?"

"Yes, *M'ija*."

Tears welled in the corners of my eyes. Cancer was in Carmen's body and she was dying. The heavy weight of longing started to pool and press into my chest. I didn't know what was worse, seeing someone die over time or in an instant, like my mom, with no warning. The sound of the car hitting her, the sight of the mangled body, my hands on her skin as I felt life slip away - the stinging memory of my mom's death wrapped its grip around my throat making it hard to breathe.

I saw Carmen's mouth move, but I couldn't hear a thing. "*M'ija*."

Carmen shook me hard and yelled. "*M'ija*, can you hear me?"

Like waking from a nightmare, I was back. Carmen knew where I went. "I miss her too, *M'ija*. I'm not going away, not anytime soon."

The pressure in my chest started to lighten. My heart no longer raced and I could breathe again. "I'm okay. I'm sorry, *Tía*."

"It's okay, *M'ija*. This is a shock for me too. But one good thing, Sumire came by earlier and took a mold of my breasts, for how they say it, posterity." Carmen rocked back and forth with a raucous laugh. "No one wants to see any part of their body torn away. I wasn't able to make a mold of my leg when I lost it to the sugar diabetes. Now with Sumire's help, I'll have a mold of my *tetas*." Carmen looked down at her breasts. "I guess I won't be needing a bra anymore, at least not a bra for two."

"When is the surgery?"

"In a couple of days. Jaime will take me."

"But you just met Jaime. I can take you."

"*M'ija*, don't be like that. I feel lots for Jaime already, and he feels the same way too. We nearly died together because of that *pinche* Ashworth. *M'ija*, he makes me feel good. I never had anybody ask me what I want, or what

I like. He wants to know how to please me. I didn't even know sex could be like this. All those years married to my husband, Mundo. He never cared about me. Jaime can touch this spot..."

It was too much for me. "Don't say it. You're my *tía*. I don't want to hear about you and Jaime."

"Okay. So we're going with you tonight, right? *Mil Máscaras* is wrestling."

"I'll take you to the Auditorium, but you guys will have to be on your own."

"No problem, *M'ija*. Maybe when you're done you'll have a little time to see *Mil Máscaras* do his stuff against Suni War Cloud, Goliath, or the Golden Greek. Oh that Golden Greek, I don't like his eyes. They spit fire *M'ija*, but *Mil* will snuff it out. I'd love to see *Mil* get the Golden Greek's head into a scissor lock, the one he can make with his legs. You've seen it, right?"

"Yeah, on TV."

Carmen snarled and grimaced as she threw her prosthetic and one good leg in the air and crossed them to show me how the Mexican wrestler would use his lower limbs to grip his opponents head into a vise grip.

"Oh *M'ija*, I'm excited. Cancer can wait. It's all about my 'Man of a Thousand Masks' tonight."

§§§§§§§

By the time I parked in the lot on 18ᵗʰ Street and Olympic Avenue, Carmen and Jaime had donned their own *Mil Máscaras* wrestling masks.

Jaime spoke with pride. "What do you think of mine, Alejandra?"

"I love that black and white spider image."

"I'm wearing the shark, *el tiburón*, *M'ija*. Like it?"

"You guys look great."

Jaime handed me a mask. "Don't think we forgot about you. Just in case you're able to join us for a couple of rounds. I call this one, *Señor Rayo*, for the lightning bolts on each side."

"Thanks, Jaime. I'll have the mask in my pocket just in case."

Carmen and Jaime left for the bouts and I cruised the perimeter of the auditorium in search of Gary Bell. After making a complete circle I couldn't find anyone with a

48

short fireplug frame, long face, and prominent square jaw. I bought a ticket to try my luck inside.

As soon as a lanky Jimmy Lennon dressed in his trademark black tuxedo stood in the center of the ring to announce the next bout, pandemonium erupted. "Tonight, in the right corner we have former champion and member of the Canadian Wrecking Crew, the Goooooolden Greeeeeek."

Jimmy Lennon held onto letters and didn't let them go as he introduced the contenders. "In the left corner from Mexico we have the 'Man of a Thousand Masks,' you know him as *Miiiiiil Máscarassssss*."

The crowd exploded. Men waved their fists in the air. Women clamored for a better view by stepping onto their seats and jumping with frenzy. Like Jaime and Carmen, many in the crowd wore traditional *Lucha Libre* masks in celebration of the free form style of wrestling that *Mil Máscaras* helped to make popular.

The two wrestlers shook hands and broke for their corners, but while *Mil Máscaras* had his back turned the Golden Greek clipped him from behind. The cheap shot brought *Mil Máscaras* to his knees. The crowd jeered and I caught myself screaming, "Boo." I wanted to keep watching but I needed to focus on finding Gary Bell.

The thick crowd made it clear I'd be hard pressed to find anyone. I tracked down a security guard. "I'm looking for Gary Bell."

"He's handling the tombs tonight."

"Tombs?"

"The locker rooms downstairs."

I nodded my appreciation. When I found the stairs I saw what had to be an older Gary Bell standing at the bottom. "Gary?"

"Yeah. Who are you?"

"I worked for John Ashworth."

"Work? Right."

Gary took his time to look me up and down. "Let me guess, he's screwing you."

A "yes" response wouldn't be entirely wrong. Ashworth had screwed me, but I knew that's not what Gary Bell meant. Nevertheless, I was happy Gary spoke in the present tense; it meant he didn't know Ashworth was dead nor the circumstances involved. I kept pace with Gary's train of thought and confirmed his assessment. "You could say that."

"What do you want?"

"I have bad news. John's dead."

Gary kept a straight face. "Haven't seen John in a while. Wouldn't really know the difference, him dead or alive. How did you find me here anyway?"

"Your wife, Patricia."

"After all these years that woman still doesn't know when to keep her mouth shut. How did you find Patricia?"

I thought quickly. "John's address book."

"Since you're here, might as well give me the details. How? When did he die?"

"Two days ago. He took his own life."

Gary laughed. "You got to be kidding me. John committed suicide? Never saw that happening, not in a million years."

"Why do you say that?"

"John thought a lot of himself. At least the John I knew."

Gary paused, "I have to check the basement out."

"Can I follow you?"

"I guess."

"How did you meet John?"

"We shared a patrol car for a short time and then we met back up working Vice."

I pulled out the photograph of Ashworth with his buddies. "Do you remember this picture?"

"Those were different days. I'd only been on the force for about a year."

"Why did you lose contact with John?"

"Different interests. Look, why all the questions?"

"Trying to piece some stories together for a eulogy."

Gary was clearly agitated. "I don't have any stories."

I needed to try another angle. "That's too bad. Shirley will be disappointed."

"You talking about his ex-wife?"

I nodded.

"Wow, that woman had a hot ass on her. Too bad she had a mouth that wouldn't quit. Always nagging that one. So you're looking for stories? Any story I shared wouldn't be fit for a funeral. We weren't saints."

"What do you mean?"

"Let's just say when you work Vice opportunities to make extra cash pop up from time to time."

I saw an opening. "Is that because you came across

people in compromising positions?"

"Where did John find you anyway? He always did like 'em young."

"How young?"

"Too young for my taste. But you, you're not too young."

Gary Bell disgusted me but I needed him right now. "It sure would be nice to spend time with an old friend of John's."

"I should be done by midnight."

What was I doing? I didn't want to be alone with this guy. I had to try and get what I needed now. "Before we meet can I ask you one more question?"

"Sure."

"I found some other photos at John's. They were black and white Polaroids. In one of them a nude woman is tied to the bed with a man on top of her. Do you think the photo had something to do with finding people in compromising positions?"

"Can't help you."

Gary Bell's quick response and lack of expression told me he was holding back. I moved in closer. He could feel my breath on his cheek. "I understand if you don't want to talk about it."

Gary pulled back and fired at me. "You cheap whore. I'll wipe the floor with your ass. Get the hell out of here."

I hadn't expected the rage now spreading across Gary Bell's face. I turned and walked fast. He didn't let up. "I'll beat you for fun."

I couldn't create distance quick enough for my comfort. When I finally stopped I found myself in the middle of a hallway that opened onto a bank of unused locker rooms. In my desperation to get away from Gary Bell I made a wrong turn and got lost. Unlike the chaos upstairs, the basement was eerily quiet with no one in sight. As I turned to retrace my steps the lights went out. The darkness made it clear why they called this place the tombs; the porous concrete walls around me closed in and sealed me in like a leaden crypt.

I had to keep calm and not panic. I knew if I stayed my course I would eventually find the stairs. I reached into my pocket and applied a cool layer of lipstick. The oily film now coating my lips filled me with a sense of power and strength, and not too soon. A couple of steps into my stride I heard the sound of footsteps echo out of the blackness. I ran and the footsteps behind me kept pace. It had to be Bell on my ass. As I raced down the hall I could see light descending out of a stairwell. I quickly turned and climbed the two flights of stairs as fast as I could. When I reached the main floor I shot out of a tunnel and onto a narrow path lined with cheering wrestling fans on both sides. I threw on the *Lucha Libre* mask with lightning bolts, the one Jaime gave me, to blend with the crowd. The teeming hoard of people lining both sides of the path wouldn't let me break through. I could hear Bell on my heels making loud guttural sounds. I turned to see he had donned his own *Lucha Libre* mask with an image of a wolf. No one was helping me. Instead I heard the crowd start to mimic Bell's animal sounds, and then I realized I was on the contender's runway, making a beeline for the ring.

I reached the edge of the ring with no choice but to pull myself up using the ringside ropes to join the Golden Greek and *Mil Máscaras*. Johnny Lennon reached for his microphone and announced the Wolfman at which point the man chasing me entered the ring. The crowd went crazy. The auditorium seemed to levitate from the deafening cheers. It hadn't been Gary Bell chasing me at all.

Johnny Lennon shot a puzzled look my way. I could see Lennon's mind scramble as he improvised. "And joining the Wolfman tonight is his special guest, Canine Thunderrrrrrr."

I was in trouble now. I walked over to Johnny and tried to explain but it was too late. *Mil Máscaras* grabbed me from behind and with one hand lifted me up and spun me as if I were a clump of pizza dough. He then threw me into the air and caught me with his legs before I hit the ground. Unable to move I could see the Wolfman preparing to mount an attack as he bounced off the ropes and landed, full body, onto *Mil*'s chest. The full weight of the Wolfman forced *Mil* to release his leg hold on me. That's when the Golden Greek pivoted and set his sights in my direction. As Carmen had described, the Greek's eyes spat fire. I needed to quickly get out of the ring. I put my gymnastics training to use. I threw my head back and let my body follow in one smooth move to catapult me into a series of back flips that brought me to the edge of the ropes. The crowd was relentless in their applause and I could hear them chant, "Thunder, Thunder, Thunder," but no matter how much they cheered they couldn't keep me in the ring. I grabbed the top rope and used it to fling away from the bout.

Carmen and Jaime were there to greet me ringside. "*M'ija*, what the hell is going on? Are you okay?"

"I thought Gary Bell had turned into the Wolfman."

"*M'ija*, did you get hit hard on the head? You're talking crazy stuff right now. No one can turn into a Wolfman *M'ija*, not without a full moon."

"No jokes right now. I'll explain later, just get me home.

"Of course *M'ija*, home it is."

Chapter 7

STRAIGHT SHOT ON THE ROCKS

I picked up the ringing phone. It was Harriett. "I happened to walk by when the receptionist took a message for you. A woman by the name of Patricia Bell phoned. She's hot. The receptionist tried to calm her, but no luck. This woman wants you to meet her tonight at her job, Lucky's Bar in Rampart, west of downtown. Alejandra, is there anything to worry about?"

"No, I'll take care of it."

§§§§§§§

At the corner of a lonely bank of houses off Beverly Boulevard sat Lucky's Bar. The blinking neon sign that read "Cold Beer" in the window was about the only thing that suggested life existed inside. Before I even stepped foot in the place the acrid smell of stale cigarettes and day old liquor jarred my nostrils. I took one deep breath and pushed through a black curtain that covered the entrance. I immediately spotted Patricia behind the bar serving a drink to an older man busy using matchbooks to build a structure of sorts. When I reached the counter, she motioned for me to take a seat at the end of the bar away from the other patrons. She wasted little time approaching me. The hot glare in her eye told me to be prepared for a tongue lashing, maybe more.

"You see this?" She pointed to the black eye she tried to hide with a caked layer of beige make-up concealer. She didn't let up. "This is your fault. I'm lucky he didn't kill me."

"I'm sorry. I never meant for anything to happen to you. I found him at the Olympic like you told me. I told him Ashworth was dead and asked him about a couple of photos I found. The man went crazy."

I could see Patricia's face relax. "So you got a taste of the bastard?"

"Sure did."

Like turning a switch Patricia's voice softened. "He's really more bark than bite."

"That black eye on your face says something different."

"It's the only thing he knows. His father and mother

used to beat him. I guess you could say he learned his ways from his parents."

"I don't think you asked me here to convince me Gary Bell is a great guy. Did you?"

"No, I didn't. The photo you described to him got him real scared. I know Gary well enough to know that when he's scared he turns into a crazy man. He can't control what he's feeling. I guess that's why I still love him."

"What did he say to you?"

"He couldn't believe John was dead. He told me John would never take his own life unless he had to."

"What do think he meant by that?"

"I asked if he thought John killed himself because he couldn't bear some sort of pain. He looked at me as if I were nuts. Told me I had it all wrong, that John had to kill himself or be killed. He said the photo you described was the reason, and that the father and the son would be coming after him now that John was dead."

"Who are the father and the son?"

"I asked him, but he didn't answer."

"What happened between the two of them? Why did John stop talking to Gary?"

"I don't know. They used to be close. When Gary worked with John he even spent all his free time with the man. Shit, I never saw my own husband. Then one day John shut him out. Gary never told me what happened. But secretly, I was happy they weren't friends anymore."

"How so?"

"There was something not right about John. I didn't like the fact that John took advantage of Gary's gambling habit to convince him to blackmail people. Gary told me when they'd bust a whorehouse sometimes they'd find important people they could pressure for money. Gary was always in need of cash." Patricia pointed to her black eye. "After Gary hit me he told me he regretted the blackmailing and the other stuff John got him mixed up in."

"What other stuff?"

"I don't know. He never talked about it."

"Patricia, do you know where I can find Gary? If he's in danger then maybe I can get him to go to the police."

"Gary? Go to the police? There's no way he'd ever do that. He's got too much pride. He blames LAPD for taking away his pension."

"Why doesn't he blame you? Didn't you report him

to LAPD Internal Affairs in the first place?"

"How do you know about that?"

"It was Internal Affairs who helped me find you."

"Huh, I don't expect you to understand. In the end Gary understood I did what I had to do, but that still didn't give LAPD the right to take away what he worked hard to earn."

"You're right, I don't understand. Regardless, do you know where I can find him? I think he may be in danger. Right now, I just want to help."

"I do still love him. I want him safe. Don't let him know you got this from me. He's staying at the Cecil Hotel, 6th and Main."

§§§§§§§

When I made the call to Captain Allen he agreed to meet me at the Cecil Hotel. I sure didn't want to be by myself when I talked to Gary again. When I arrived a sea of patrol cars and a coroner's van were parked outside. I had a gut feeling everyone was here for the man I needed to question.

"Alejandra."

I turned to find Captain Allen. "What's this all about?"

"Gary Bell is dead."

"No, no, no."

"A cleaning lady found Bell in the bathtub. The detective on the case is thinking suicide or accident."

I was emphatic. "Not possible."

"We'll have to leave that up to the medical examiner, although from a quick look at the scene I'd have to agree with you."

"Tell me more."

"I saw a hot pastrami sandwich in the room, warm to the touch and out of its wrapper. Not sure why a guy would buy a sandwich and get ready to eat it if he planned to take a bath."

"I knew it. I just left Patricia Bell. She told me Gary was scared. He knew someone would come after him."

"Why did he think that?"

"I found Gary working at the Olympic Auditorium. I told him about Ashworth committing suicide."

"Did you tell him why?"

"No. I didn't tell him he did it to avoid prison for running a sex trade operation. But I did ask him about some photographs and that's when he got real angry. I thought he'd kill me."

"What photos? Like the one you showed me?"

"No, others. I don't want to say more. I can't say more."

"Alejandra, I can't help you if you don't tell me what's going on."

"Look, I appreciate what you've done for me already, but..."

"But what? I owe Harriett everything. I told her I'd do all I can to help you."

Captain Allen could see the apprehension in my face. "You don't trust me. Why would you after what Ashworth put you through? Alejandra, I'm not John Ashworth."

I paused and relented. "Captain Allen, I broke into a house and found some photographs."

"Whose house? Start from the beginning."

"I followed Detective Carr, the one investigating the Belvedere Park murders. He drove to Ashworth's house to conduct a search and when he left I used an open bathroom window to get inside. I found three photographs, the one I showed you and these two."

I handed over the photographs to Captain Allen. "After talking with Gary Bell's wife, I'm almost certain Gary and John Ashworth were blackmailing the men in these photos. Patricia told me Bell and Ashworth were involved in extortion."

A look of shock panned over Captain Allen's face. "Who else has seen these?"

"Harriett. She told me the older man is Judge Thomas, and the younger man, we don't know. Gary's death has to be linked to these photos and the Belvedere Park murders. Otherwise, it's too much of a coincidence. I think someone knows I went to see Bell and I think he was murdered because he knew something."

"That may be, but it's not as if these photos can be used as evidence given how you got them."

"I know, but if it weren't for me the photos would still be hidden in Ashworth's house."

"I'll see what I can do on my end. I'll try and talk to the detective on Bell's case. But I'll tell you right now I won't get much. My colleagues don't like Internal Affairs, which means they'll be unwilling to answer my questions. They think I'm out to betray them and they are often right."

"Don't people want answers?"

"Homicide detectives like cases that get solved and then cleared from their desks. I should know. I was one."

"Don't they care about the victims?"

"Honestly, Alejandra, there are too many victims. Even the ones who get prioritized, detectives can't afford to feel anything. The only way to survive the depravity is to put up a wall. Otherwise, the horror consumes you. I'm not going to make excuses for detectives who should try harder, but even if we assume these photos are tied to Gary's death then what you have is a potential rabbit hole with no end in sight."

"You're wrong. I know where the hole ends."

"Where?"

"At the gates of Hell."

Chapter 8

CIPHER

"*M'ija*, are you home?"

"Coming, Carmen."

I walked in from my outdoor patio to see Carmen and Sumire both dressed in bright yellow dresses with sun hats to match.

"*M'ija*, Sumire and I are going shopping. Want to join us?"

"I don't have the right outfit."

"Aren't these dresses cute, *M'ija*? Sumire made them for us. We're like a couple of blooming daisies."

Carmen choked on her last word and started to cry.

"*Tía*, what is it?"

"Bad luck, Jaime asked me to marry him. I'm going to die right after I found a man who really loves me: all 202 pounds of me."

"Remember what you told me? You've got a lot of living to do. The doctors are going to remove the cancer. All of it. If anyone can survive this it's you, *Tía*."

"Oh *M'ija*, I hope you're right."

"I'm glad you have Jaime."

Carmen took a shallow breath. "I want you with me when my time is close. Dying can be cruel *M'ija*, especially when death makes you feel all the pain of this world before it takes you. It's not like when we're born. Birth has mercy on us. It keeps us from remembering how it feels to be pushed through a tiny narrow *chocha*. And you know I don't like small spaces. What's the word for it?"

"Claustrophobia."

"That's it. I have claustrophobia. I'm happy I don't remember my birth, but my mom didn't feel the same way. She reminded me all the time of the pain I put her through. Telling me my head was too big. That no woman should ever have to endure what she did. Some women shouldn't be mothers, especially when they can't replace pain with joy. Anyway, you coming with us?"

"Of course, I'll come. Can we stop to get something to eat?"

"Now you're speaking my language."

As we neared the neighboring shopping district the smell of roasted *elote* ignited a grumbling in my gut.

Without a pause we each paid twenty-five cents for a grilled ear of corn skewered on a stick and dripping with butter. I garnished my treat with lime and a sprinkling of chili powder before taking my first bite. A flood of warm, tangy sweetness filled my mouth and within a couple of minutes my cob was bare.

"Where are we off to now?"

"Well *M'ija*, Sumire needs candy and I need shoe laces."

Sumire added to the list. "I also need food for Gato. He likes that new cat food brand, the one with the giant roaring lion on the package. He's sold on the advertising."

"Sumire, he's a cat. He doesn't know what's on the package." I said.

"Gato knows more than you think."

I didn't know why I tried to disagree. Sumire's cat, Gato, could do remarkable things. In her own right, Sumire was amazing too. I didn't know if she had an innate gift or learned it growing up in a Japanese internment camp, but she could see things no one else could.

Our first stop was the candy store. Sumire's request today was ten bags of M&M's. The owner loved seeing

Sumire. "I love that you always pick my candy. You know these were named after me. M and M for Manaka Makaido. My favorite color is yellow like your dress and the sun."

Sumire responded. "Without sunlight there's no color and no beautiful world to see."

We left and headed to Joe's. The large green high-heeled shoe that jutted from the building's façade read, Epstein Shoe Repair. Inside my senses were overtaken by the sight and smell of all things leather. Beyond the cash register I could see Joe Epstein at his workbench. He finished hammering a heel onto a boot and lumbered toward us. "Good afternoon Ladies, Joe Epstein at your service. How have you all been? I haven't seen you in a while. Are your soles in need of salvation today?"

Carmen laughed and answered, "Just a pair of brown laces, Joe."

Joe reached above his back counter to pull down the package. "That'll be an even forty cents for the laces. No cost for the smile. That's free for you, Carmen."

Joe Epstein was one of the happiest people I had ever met and he had good reason. When I was a kid Joe told me the Nazis forced him to board a railroad freight car along with others from his Warsaw neighborhood. Somehow Joe got on the train without a Nazi guard checking his weathered wooden cobbler box, which had an awl and stretching pliers in a bottom compartment. As soon as the train pulled out of the yard Joe set to work with his tools to pry open the bars on the lone window inside the car. Joe freed himself along with ten others that day.

Carmen put exact change on the counter and that's when I noticed the sign behind the register. "Hey Joe, do you still use the Capitol phone exchange?"

"Of course I do, I like the ring of it. I enjoy saying Capitol for the letters CA instead of 22. Then I add the last five digits for my phone number. Why have letters on the dial face of a phone if you're not going to use them?"

"I agree. You've made me happy, Joe, more than you can know."

"Well, good, I like everyone to leave here happy."

On the way to the Birds of a Feather pet store Carmen couldn't hold back her curiosity. "*M'ija*, since when do you get so excited over a phone number?"

"It's not just the number, it's that he uses the exchange. One of the murder victims etched five numbers into his leather belt, and to do it he had to really stretch his bound hands to make sure those numbers followed the name, ED, imprinted on the belt."

"So *M'ija*, you think ED represents an exchange?"

"It's worth a shot. Maybe I'll get lucky. Dial a number and get a murderer."

Sumire couldn't contain her excitement. "Let's go now, straight home, and dial. No time to stop for cat food. Gato will understand."

Once home I picked up the receiver and dialed. Using the phone's dial face I saw that both letters, E and D, corresponded to the number three. I followed them with the five I got from the leather belt. After four rings a recorded voice came on the line, "You have reached a number that is no longer in service. Please check the number and dial again."

I followed the directions, but no luck, the recorded voice was all I got.

Chapter 9

CLEAR AS WATER

I was happy to see Olivia when I arrived at the morgue. "I'm glad you're here. Hope you have something that can give me traction with the case."

"Alejandra, I was just starting to tell Armand what I found. I was able to analyze the tooth and bone samples. Turns out all the men, except for the eldest victim, were born and spent much of the last ten years of their lives in the same place: the south-eastern part of Mexico; most likely the state of Chiapas."

"And the eldest victim?" I asked.

He was from the north-eastern part of the country; the state of Coahuila."

With excitement and confidence Armand announced, "Oh my, I think that explains the Leukonychia striata."

Armand walked over to the freezer, opened a drawer, and pulled out the tray with the eldest victim. He called us over. "See the fingernails on this man? He has white bands running across his nails. I didn't make much of it at first, but now knowing where he's from it's likely arsenic poisoning caused the striations."

"*Primo*, are you thinking what I'm thinking?"

"You got it. We're on the same page."

Impatiently I chimed in, "I want to be on the page with you."

Armand explained, "Our Uncle, *Tío* Enrique, was from a town in the north-eastern part of Coahuila called San Juan de Sabinas. Practically every man in that town, like our *tío*, worked at the coal mine. *Tío* Enrique told us horror stories about his work in that mine. Even though he left that town and moved to Los Angeles, the mine never let *Tío* go. The daily exposure to coal dust and the arsenic used to process the coal took him away from us too soon. This man must have been a coal miner. I'd bank on it, especially since this victim also showed the type of lung damage that comes from breathing toxic particulate matter day in and day out."

Even though I was no closer to knowing who the men were or why they were killed, Armand and Olivia had given me an important lead.

"This gives me something. Do you think you can take

74

a picture of each of these men for me?"

"Sure thing."

"Great, I'm going to need them for my trip to San Juan de Sabinas."

"Alejandra, how do you feel about me going with you? I have some time coming to me and I think I can help. I know someone in Sabinas we can talk to."

"I'd like that, Armand. I'd like it a lot."

"Perfect, and by the time we get back maybe Olivia will have some more results for us."

Olivia playfully cut in, "Is that how it's going to be? You both go off to have fun and leave Olivia to do the work."

"*Prima*, you know it's not like that, but it sure would be great to have the results from the blood samples ready when we get back."

Confused, I asked. "What blood samples?"

Olivia explained, "I'm trying out this new technique in the lab, I call it DNA, deoxyribonucleic acid, fingerprinting. Armand thought it might be worthwhile not only to analyze the victim's teeth and bone for their oxygen content, but also their DNA."

I had a million questions. "DNA, do you mean chromosomes?"

"Yes and no. In every human cell, except for sperm and egg cells, there are 46 chromosomes, and each chromosome is comprised of DNA. Most of the DNA that each of us possess is identical, but there's a small percentage of our DNA that is more variable and therefore more likely to be different between individuals who aren't related. I've been playing around with a way to look at particular chromosome regions that have been identified to contain highly variable DNA sequences."

"I see. The DNA variability is much like the impressions that can be made from our fingertips." I said.

"You got it, but I predict with DNA fingerprinting the possibilities will be unmatched. We aren't there yet, but within a few years we should be able to isolate and analyze DNA from a drop of blood left at a crime scene. My analysis will be limited but I should still be able to see if any of the victims are related."

"I'll be ready for anything you can offer, Olivia."

"Let's keep our fingers crossed. I'm off to the lab. I'll see you two later."

Much time hadn't passed but I hoped Armand had some news on Gary Bell. "Anything on the drowning case?"

"There's no way I can call this one with any certainty."

"How can that be?"

"Determining whether a drowning is an accident, suicide, or murder is nearly impossible. The initial blood work shows he had a lot of liquor in his system so he could have drowned accidentally. And..." Armand paused, "...he was dressed."

"What does that mean?" I asked.

"A murderer will usually go out of his way to make a drowning look like an accident by undressing his victim."

"So you're telling me Bell wasn't murdered."

"I just don't know. If he drowned while alive and conscious I'd expect to see defense wounds, but there are none. I tried to determine if someone rendered him unconscious and then placed him in a tub of water to make it look like an accidental drowning."

"And?"

"Around the nose and mouth I found some paleness that could have occurred because of pressure caused by someone smothering him. But the discoloration is so slight, I can't be certain."

"How do you rule out suicide? How do know if Bell

was dead or alive before his body hit the water?"

"Water in the lungs usually indicates the person was alive, conscious or unconscious, before he drowned. There's no water in Bell's lungs."

"So he was killed before being placed in the tub."

"Not so fast. In a small number of people we've seen death result from what's called dry drowning; water doesn't get into the lungs in those cases. It happens when the vocal cords spasm causing the throat to constrict, sealing off the airway. Bell died from a dry drowning that resulted in cardiac arrest. I can't tell if he was dead or alive before he went under water. The cause of death has to be classified as undetermined."

"Armand, what about his shoes?"

"What do you mean?"

"Are Gary Bell's shoes still here?"

"Yes."

"I remember thinking about them when I saw his body being removed from his room. I wondered how white scuff marks got on the heels of those beautifully polished shoes. I forgot all about them until now."

"Let's take a look."

Armand examined the shoes. "Looks like painted plaster."

"Had he been dragged to the tub his shoes could have scraped against the wall."

"Good point. I'll bring it up to the detective. Maybe he can find evidence in Bell's room to corroborate, but I wouldn't count on it. The detective seemed pretty determined to close the case."

"Damn it, doesn't anybody care?"

"Alejandra, I care."

"I know you do. I guess in the end it doesn't really matter how Gary Bell died. He's dead and he can't help us. Now we have to hope Sabinas gives us an open door to something more concrete."

Armand looked at me, affectionately. "Are you sure you're in the right line of work?"

"What are you talking about?"

"It seems like private detective is more up your alley."

"Hmm, Alex Marisol, Private Investigator. I like the sound of it."

"Why Alex and not Alejandra?"

"I'd get more business if people thought they were reaching out to a man."

"But the cat would be out of the bag once they saw you."

"Sure, but if they didn't like what they saw I'd still have a chance to work my charm before they turned away."

Armand leaned in. "The way you worked your charm on me?"

I inched closer. "Dr. Gomez, I think it was the other way around."

This time I turned my head into his neck and breathed in his smell of sweet and salted musk. I couldn't get enough. I wanted to bathe in him. I parted my lips and pulled his mouth toward mine. I felt us both surrender. There was no better taste.

Chapter 10

EL GUSANO

We wasted little time securing a rent-a-car after flying into Laredo, Texas. Armand drove while I navigated the map and charted our two-hour drive into Mexico across the Rio Grande River. Barring any complications, I figured we could make it to Sabinas and the home of Nacho Candelaria before nightfall. Armand's Aunt Trini, *Tío* Enrique's surviving wife, arranged for us to meet Nacho, a tender and good soul as she had described. From the little I knew Nacho spent years working alongside *Tío* Enrique in the mines. He had even risked his own life to dig Enrique out of a pile of rubble after high levels of methane gas created an explosion, which killed twelve of their friends. Trini told us Nacho still knew a lot of men, *los mineros*, who worked the mine. I hoped Nacho could help by knowing some or all of the men found murdered in the truck bed.

By the time we arrived our Ford Pinto no longer looked white. The dust we stirred driving the unpaved roads left an uninterrupted brown film over the car's entire frame.

Hearing our car, Nacho emerged from his house to greet us.

"*Bienvenidos*. Welcome, Armand and Alejandra. I'm so happy, *muy feliz*. I hope it's okay for me to speak English while you are here, I don't get much chance since my father died."

I asked, "You grew up speaking English?"

"Yes, my father was from *Tejas*. Even though we lived here he wanted me to know English."

Nacho's voice was warm and inviting. I immediately wanted to know all about him. "When did your father move here from Texas?"

"Alejandra, it's dangerous to ask an old man about the past. History is my friend and I'm not stingy when it comes to words. It could be a long night."

"We have nowhere to go until tomorrow."

"Good. Come inside, I'll pour you a drink and fill your ears."

We followed Nacho inside and took seats at a weathered wooden table.

"I hope you like mezcal." Nacho placed a filled shot glass in front of each of us. "Food will be ready soon, I made *mole*. It's the one thing I can cook that tastes good. My wife, *mi amor* Imelda, she did most of the cooking, but she passed last year."

Armand responded, "Aunt Trini told me about Imelda. I'm sorry. We didn't expect you to make us dinner, but it sure smells good. Thank you."

"You're the nephew of my good friend, Enrique. I would have given my life for him. *Comida* and mezcal are nothing. Drink up."

As I let the agave derived spirit pickle my throat I realized I hadn't spent enough time acquiring a taste for the stuff. Nacho quickly refilled my glass and I realized there'd be no casual introduction; I would be spending intimate time with tequila's cousin.

My questions about the murdered men would have to wait. In keeping with his warning Nacho immediately immersed us in family history. "This is a picture of my father as a young boy. He's standing with my grandfather, my namesake, Ignacio Candelaria. The picture was taken in 1852, just before they stole my grandfather's *rancho*."

I pressed, "How does someone steal a ranch?"

"Manifest Destiny."

Armand asked for clarification. "Are you referring to

the United States' aggressive land grab?"

"You know about it. It was disguised as The Treaty of Guadalupe Hidalgo, signed to end the Mexican-American War. What a crime! That treaty created a new border for Texas along the Rio Grande and it called for Mexico to give up California, Arizona, New Mexico, and parts of Colorado, Nevada and Utah in exchange for little money."

Armand added to the history lesson. "Aunt Trini's family, as far back as they could remember, lived in California. They were *Californios*, native Californians. They eventually lost their land because of that treaty."

"So you know firsthand how greed works. For my grandfather, one thief by the name of Samuel Buchanan changed his fate. Even though the treaty recognized Spanish and Mexican land grants, Buchanan knew Mexicans like my grandfather had no political power to hold on to property after it became part of the United States."

Nacho took a sip of mezcal, "Samuel Buchanan used all his means to get what he wanted. Late one night he went to my grandfather's ranch with a group of men who were former Texas Rangers. They grabbed my grandfather and grandmother out of bed and dragged them outside. They forced my father, a young boy, to watch as they whipped my grandfather and raped my grandmother. They threatened to return the next night unless my grandfather signed over his property." Nacho stared at the photo of his father and grandfather. "Humans are like parasites. They are incapable of surviving without taking over a host."

"Do you know what became of Buchanan?" I asked.

"He followed in his father's footsteps and became a very rich man."

I followed with another question. "Who was his father?"

"A former slave trader from Missouri by the name of James Buchanan. He made his money trading African slaves with the likes of James Bowie and Jean Lafitte."

"Jean Lafitte the pirate?" Armand asked.

I was dumbfounded. "How do you know all of this?"

"I needed to understand the history that led to the loss of my grandfather's land. The more I learned, the more I realized Samuel Buchanan's greed descended from his father. You've heard the saying the fruit doesn't fall far from the tree?"

"Yes." Armand and I answered in unison.

"In the case of James and Samuel, they were part of the same fruit: Samuel the seed and James the flesh surrounding him. When eight-year-old Samuel Buchanan learned his father had died defending the Alamo he filled his heart with hatred and disgust for Mexicans. Samuel didn't care that Mexican *Tejanos*, who had called *Tejas* their home for generations, had also been killed fighting the Mexican army for independence. When the United States declared war on Mexico in 1846 Samuel Buchanan was one of the first in line to draw Mexican blood. He was ruthless. As a Texas Ranger he raided Mexican villages, set homes ablaze, raped women, hanged innocent civilian men, and shot children all in the name of securing a U.S. victory. Buchanan and his Ranger compatriots became notorious for their brutality. They lived up to the name the Mexicans had given them, *Los Diablos Tejanos* or Texas Devils."

"Nacho, have you ever taught history?" I asked.

"This house is my classroom."

I wanted more. "What happened to your grandparents after losing their land?"

"They came here and started again from nothing. Times were hard. All they had was agave. They ate the flowers, the stalks, and the sap. Catching and cooking up rodents was a treat for them. Things began to turn around when the coal mine opened. By that time my father was old enough to work and his wages helped put better food on the table and build this house. I don't remember a single day when my father didn't have a layer of black coal dust on his face and hands. My father wanted a different life for me. He didn't want me in the mines. He thought an education would protect me from the evil men in this world. But as I've learned, the only thing that protects you from the devil is being lucky enough not to cross his path. Evil is everywhere. Coming back home after my studies was just as good as any other place. Plus, Imelda was here and she didn't want to leave. She was *mi amor y mi vida*, my love and my life, from the day we met. I never regretted my decision to return and work the mines. I knew I could leave any time with the power of my mind. Books became my way of visiting the world outside of this town. I read about everything imaginable through Faulkner, Woolf, Calvino, Rilke, Neruda, Cervantes, I can go on and on. Words allowed me to transcend these walls, *como el gusano*."

Nacho had lost me. "Like the worm?"

"Yes, like the worm in this mezcal."

Nacho emptied the last bit of mezcal into my glass along with the worm that had settled at the bottom of the bottle.

"The worm in your glass is actually a larva preserved in one stage of its life. No longer capable of metamorphosis on its own. But once inside you, like the words on the page of a book, the larva will undergo a transformation, sprouting wings and taking flight. You'll have no choice but to get carried along."

Nacho's stories had held me captive and I had been their willing prisoner. I had expected to arrive, ask him a few questions, and leave.

"I think the *mole* is ready. Let me serve your plates."

Nacho returned from the kitchen with plates of chicken submerged in a smooth, dark brown sauce. The delicious aroma rose off my plate and I didn't hesitate to slice away a succulent piece of the breast meat for my first bite. The heat from the chili in the sauce rolled across the roof of my mouth and opened my senses to the taste of cocoa, cinnamon, peanuts, and garlic. My taste buds danced with delight.

"Please, you both traveled too far to hear me ramble on. How can this old man help you with your investigation?"

"Armand brought some photos for you to see. They're of five murdered men we believe are from this town."

Armand passed the photos to Nacho who proceeded to slowly shuffle through them.

"Do you recognize any of the men?" Armand asked.

"I know this man very well."

Nacho pointed to the photo of the eldest victim. "That's Eduardo Cuevas. He had a big mouth, that one. He always talked about leaving this place and making lots of money in the North. Then one day he told he met *el comedor del pescado grande*: his ticket to fortune."

Confused I asked. "The big fish eater?"

"I never knew what he meant. He always talked in riddles. It was his way of saying something that meant nothing, so I paid no mind."

"Where did he meet *el comedor*?"

"Eduardo said he met him in Los Angeles when he was visiting a friend. I always assumed that's where he moved. He left about two years ago and took several young miners with him."

Nacho pointed to the other photos. "These are the men who went with him. He promised them a rich life."

"Do you know their names?" I asked.

"No, they were real but invisible."

"What do you mean?"

"They all arrived together from the South not able to speak a word of Spanish. They were Native Mexican Indians. They may as well have been vermin the way everyone treated them. I tried to get to know them, but it was too late. Like the spider using its web to snare prey, Eduardo Cuevas used his limited knowledge of their language to take advantage of them. He manipulated them so they would trust him and only him."

"Did any family travel with them from the South?"

"No, they arrived from Chiapas alone."

I turned to Armand. "Did you hear that? Nacho just corroborated Olivia's test results. The younger men did grow up in Chiapas."

Armand challenged me, "Sure, but what good does it do us? We have no lead to follow."

"Yes, we do. We know Eduardo Cuevas took the men to Los Angeles. We just have to find out why."

"Would there be anybody who could tell us more about these men, Nacho?" I asked.

"Not anyone from here. They worked all day and then went home with Eduardo. If you could find the man they all left with, that might help."

"They left with another man from here?"

"He wasn't from here. He came, packed everyone into a van, and left the same day."

"What did he look like?"

"He was a white man. I remember his head was long for his body."

I pulled out the group picture with Ashworth and Gary Bell. "Do you see the man in this photo?"

"When I saw him he was much older, but it's the man on the end." Nacho pointed to Gary Bell.

"That's helpful. One more thing, all of the victims had one of their arms ripped off. Do you have any idea why someone would do that?"

Nacho rolled up his sleeve. On the inner part of his forearm there was a small tattoo. It showed a crisscrossed pick and shovel with the word Sabinas written at the top. "Most of us miners, including Eduardo Cuevas, had one of these. Maybe the killer knew it would tie him to Sabinas."

"Did the younger men have the same tattoo?" I asked with urgency.

"I doubt it. We get this tattoo as a symbol of honor, for giving our life over to the earth. Those other men weren't here long enough to earn the right, but who knows what Eduardo had them do. They were like innocent lambs doing whatever the wolf told them, for fear of being eaten."

"This is the second time a tattoo may hold an important key in this case."

Nacho questioned, "When was the first?"

"An earlier victim, a man by the name of Sergio Guerra, had a tattoo of a *calavera* on his tongue. That tattoo ultimately led us to Sergio's friends and then put us on path with a cold-blooded killer, Detective John Ashworth."

"A policeman?"

"Yes, and even though Ashworth is dead the killing hasn't ended. Someone is still out there."

"That means you'll need to have a little more mezcal. I have a special bottle. One with an extra large *gusano* for luck."

"Of course Nacho, but only if you tell us more stories."

"I can do more than that."

Nacho reached for his accordion and slipped it on. He set to work on his keys while expanding and compressing the bellows to create high-pitched harmonized vibrations.

"This is one of my favorites, a *Cumbia.*"

The fiery tune brought Armand to his feet. He reached for my arm. "Time to dance the *Cumbia*, Alejandra."

I stood and melted into Armand's body. He wrapped his right arm tight around my waist and led me with his left hand across the living room floor as Nacho sang.

"La cumbia pa' que bailen con ganas
La cumbia pa' que bailen con ganas"

There was no doubt I lived the words Nacho was singing; dancing the *Cumbia* with desire. It would be just a matter of time before Armand and I would have to excuse ourselves so our bodies could engage in a different dance, a more intimate one.

Chapter 11

BEYOND FACE VALUE

When we arrived back in Los Angeles, I realized Armand was right. Even though Nacho identified Gary Bell and Eduardo Cuevas from photos, I had no lead to follow since both men were dead. I had nowhere to turn except for a visit to Detective Carr.

My attempts to speak with Carr on the phone got me nowhere. The detective made it clear he wanted nothing to do with me, but I wouldn't take no for an answer. Determined to talk with him, I drove to the Sheriff's Homicide Bureau and sat parked in my car. At 5:30 am, Carr arrived. I approached quickly, cutting off his path to the front door.

"Detective, can I talk to you?"

Carr didn't waste words. "I'm busy."

"I know, but if you could spare a minute. Please."

"One minute." Carr lifted his arm and stared at his wristwatch.

"Really, Detective."

"You said one minute, tick tock, tick tock."

I spoke quickly. "I came from a small town in Mexico, Sabinas-Hidalgo. It looks like the murdered men worked the mines in that town. The older victim, his name, was Eduardo Cuevas. He brought the younger men to the U.S. with the help of Gary Bell, a friend of Ashworth's and former LAPD detective."

"Your time is up. This case is closed."

"What do you mean?"

"What you've just said makes the case against Ashworth even stronger. Ashworth's friend brought the men here from Mexico and Ashworth killed them. The victims' time of death doesn't rule Ashworth out as a prime suspect. He could have committed the murders well before he took his own life. Plus, Ashworth's prints were found all over that truck. We have our man. The case is closed."

"Even if Ashworth did do it, you don't have the whole story."

"The LAPD accomplices we have in custody corroborate Ashworth's role."

"What accomplices? Did you speak with Detective Nadel?"

"Yes, we did. He told us Ashworth was responsible for all of it."

"Did you search Nadel's house?"

"Of course we did. We found nothing. I'm not wasting any more time with you."

As Carr started to walk away, I moved in front of him. "Don't you care? Detective Nadel must know something. He helped to run the sex ring with Ashworth."

"If you don't get out of my way you'll find yourself in a jail cell."

I moved to the side and Carr moved ahead. He turned back once to glare in my direction before entering the Bureau's doors.

§§§§§§

Carr was closing the case and I knew there was still someone out there, somebody other than Ashworth who was pulling the strings and calling the shots behind the scenes. My mind felt hazy and confused. I needed to collect my thoughts and I needed to eat. Even though the sun hadn't crested over the horizon I knew The Pantry would be open for business. I headed to 9th Street and Figueroa. It took less than ten minutes to clear my plate of skillet fried potatoes, two sunny side-up eggs, and a thick slice of grilled sourdough toast. The waiter commended me on my hearty appetite and tallied my bill. I saw him write the total, $1.85.

The waiter sparked my attention. "Would you mind writing the total again, but slower?"

"I'm not even gonna ask why. Here you go."

The waiter rewrote the total and I saw it again. "Wow."

"Wow, what?"

"I've never seen anyone write the number eight like you do. You write the number three and then loop it from the bottom to connect it to a backward number three."

"Never thought about it. Done it that way my whole life."

"Thank you, thank you so much." I plucked down a full dollar tip.

"I'll write the number eight all day for you for this kind of money. Thank ya, Miss."

I walked out of the restaurant and located a telephone booth. I dropped a dime and dialed. As I did before I used the two letters found on Eduardo Cuevas' belt, ED, as part of the Edison exchange. I followed the exchange with the five numbers scratched into leather belt, but this time using an eight instead of a three for the last number. After four rings a woman answered, "Saint Basil's Rectory." I didn't know what to say so I hung up the phone.

I had heard of St. Basil's. A lavish church fit for its upscale neighborhood; that's how I remembered it described. I needed to know why Eduardo Cuevas would use his last moments on Earth to leave a number to St. Basil's. The first order of business was to find out who ran the place.

Chapter 12

A MAN OF ONE ROBE

As expected, Harriett was seated in her office. What I didn't anticipate was to find Rocky at her side. I also didn't expect to see the dramatic effect of their new love affair on Rocky's appearance. Aside from the steel grey hair no one would guess he was 70; he looked much younger and more fit than usual.

Harriett called to me as I approached. "Alejandra, come on in. Rocky stopped by to take me to breakfast. Didn't you, Rocky?"

"We were just getting ready to leave. Harriett knows this great place at Grand Central Market."

I was firm. "Your breakfast will have to wait."

I threw an *LA Times* article with a picture of Monsignor Crowe onto Harriett's desk. "Anything strike you?"

Confused Harriett answered, "What should I be seeing?"

"Does Monsignor Crowe remind you of anyone?"

"Like whom, can you help me out?"

I reached into my pocket and pulled out the Polaroid photo with the woman tied to the bed. "Like the naked man in this picture."

Harriett studied the image. "Hmmm, maybe it's the same man, but I can't be 100 percent certain. The man in this Polaroid has to be at least 20 years younger."

"What do you know about Monsignor Crowe?"

"I know he's the backbone of the Archdiocese, as far as money matters and real estate holdings are concerned. Crowe has a reputation for being a financial wizard and he's Cardinal McCrudden's right-hand man."

"Well, I think Crowe is somehow involved in the Belvedere Park murders."

"That's unbelievable. What kind of information do you have?"

"One of the victims scratched five numbers into his leather belt. He did it in a way that the numbers followed his name, ED, which had been stamped into the belt. When I used ED as an exchange and dialed the number I reached Saint Basil's rectory. I did a bit of research and found out Monsignor Crowe is the pastor of Saint Basil's. I found this photo of him in the *Times* archive room."

Harriett was shocked. "Oh my, this is going to catch fire if what you're saying pans out."

"There's more. Turns out the murdered men worked the mines in a Mexican town, Sabinas-Hidalgo. I met a man there who knew the men. He told me the eldest victim, Eduardo Cuevas, moved to Los Angeles to find his fortune. A person Eduardo referred to as *el comedor del pescado grande*, planned to help him make his money."

"Alejandra, you'll need to translate."

"The big fish eater."

Impatient, Harriett pushed. "More translation, please."

"What do Catholics eat every Friday?" I asked.

Harriett's mouth parted wide as she stared at me incredulously, "The Monsignor is the big fish eater?"

"That's what I'm betting on, especially since Eduardo scratched the Monsignor's number into his belt. What can you tell me about Crowe's boss, Cardinal McCrudden?"

"He's a political master."

Rocky added, "He sure is. Harriett, tell her how he bamboozled the public, ripped us off."

"Ever hear about Proposition 3, Alejandra?"

"No."

"Not surprising, you were a baby, just two or three years old. It was a 1952 referendum that went on the ballot after the Governor signed legislation to end taxation of Catholic school buildings. A taxpayer's group spearheaded the referendum in a move to reverse the legislation. McCrudden was a huge fan of the Governor's legislation. After all he'd been hard at work consolidating Catholic influence in Southern California by increasing property holdings for the Archdiocese, and he didn't want to be on the hook for paying taxes on his real estate."

Rocky cut in, "Less taxes for him meant less money for the public."

"Rocky's right. The proposition failed, saving the Archdiocese a lot of revenue. It left the City of Los Angeles and the Los Angeles Unified School District without the funding it needed to support public schools, street maintenance, you name it."

Rocky cut in again. "The Cardinal got his way."

Harriett countered, "Not right away. With support from public school advocates the tax-exempt issue went before the voters again in 1958 as Proposition 16. In the run-up to the election the Cardinal used his clout to influence politicians and citizens alike. His investment paid off. He won by a two to one margin, thereby securing tax-exempt status for his Catholic schools."

I knew the answer but asked anyway. "Does he have politicians in his pocket?"

Emphatic, Harriett answered. "Yes. Look at what happened with Chávez Ravine."

"I remember my mom talking about a friend who lost her home in Chávez Ravine. The Cardinal was involved?"

"At least indirectly, and I'm sure it secured his role as a power broker in this city for a long time to come."

Harriett had my full attention. "Go on."

"In the early '50s the Cardinal represented a voice for Catholic traditionalists. His vocal anti-communist views were no secret. He saw Soviet and Chinese influence across the globe and at home in the United States as a growing threat to Christian ideals. He even utilized the Archdiocese newspaper, *The Tidings*, to warn parishioners of the communist threat and encourage them to participate in conservative activism."

Harriett had lost me. "But how is this related to Chávez Ravine?"

"In 1951, the Los Angeles Housing Authority began acquiring land from Chávez Ravine residents, most Mexican-Americans, by forcing them to accept meager cash payments for their property to make way for Elysian Park Heights. Elysian Park Heights was a proposed housing development that would include schools and playgrounds. For residents who refused to sell, the City used the power of eminent domain to forcefully evict them. All of this was happening while the Cardinal did all he could to make sure Elysian Park Heights was never built. He regularly denounced public housing as an example of socialism. He even tied the Elysian Park Heights project to a communist plot bent on taking control of Los Angeles. The Cardinal's views held considerable sway over people who bought into anti-communist fear mongering."

Harriet paused and with a look of disgust continued. "The fate of Chávez Ravine was sealed in 1953 when Norris Poulson was elected Mayor of Los Angeles. Like the Cardinal, Poulson used the fear of communism to win the election. He campaigned on a platform promising to end the construction of any new public housing including Elysian Park Heights."

"Harriett, Dodger Stadium now stands in Chávez Ravine. Did the Cardinal play a role in that land deal?"

"You mean with the Dodger's owner, Walter O'Malley? No evidence of that, but it sure is an interesting question. I've always wondered what the outcome would have been for Chávez Ravine and its residents if the Cardinal hadn't gotten involved. But he did, and now the bucolic hillsides of Chávez Ravine are gone. There's no housing development and Walter O'Malley makes millions off his stadium. It all feels eerily unsettling when you consider that McCrudden turned down a profitable job on Wall Street to enter the priesthood. He wasted no time making his ecclesiastical ascension to become Archbishop and then Cardinal. He's created an Archdiocese more akin to a wealthy conglomerate. If he hadn't joined the priesthood I'm convinced he would have become a Wall Street magnate."

Rocky quipped. "Anti-communist fear mongering, the 'Red Scare;' it's like the circus clown."

Confused, I asked. "What do you mean?"

"The circus clown keeps the lion from eating the ringmaster. The Cardinal and Poulson used a circus clown to keep the public from eating them."

"Rocky, who's the circus clown?"

"Propaganda, Sweety. It's dirty propaganda."

"What you both are telling me might jive with what I've been thinking. Remember this photo?"

I pulled out the picture of Ashworth standing alongside fellow LAPD officers. I pointed to the man on the end. "Captain Allen identified this man. His name is Gary Bell and he was found dead a while ago. I'm betting he was murdered. I met with his estranged wife and she verified what you thought. She told me her husband and Ashworth were involved in blackmailing schemes. Harriett, if we assume Monsignor Crowe is the man in this photo then it's possible Ashworth and Bell were blackmailing him. And then comes the next question, did McCrudden know about it?"

Harriett shook her head. "Questions that need answers."

I added, "There's more. My contact in Mexico told me Gary Bell brought Eduardo Cuevas and the other Belvedere

Park murder victims to Los Angeles. The pieces are here, but I don't know how they fit together."

Rocky interjected, "Well Ladies, I know someone who might be able to help. My friend, William Dubin, is a former priest who had run-ins with McCrudden. They didn't like each other, and if I remember right he told me their troubles started around Chávez Ravine. He may be able to give you info on McCrudden and if nothing else tell you if the man in the Polaroid is Crowe or not."

I questioned, "How did you meet a former priest?"

"I met William after my friend Viola was murdered."

"Viola?" I asked.

"Viola Liuzzo. She was killed right around the time your mom died. I didn't know her long. We met in 1965 during a demonstration in Alabama working with our black friends to win everyone's right to vote."

Harriett stroked Rocky's arm. "I remember the time as if it were yesterday. I'm sorry about Viola."

"Thanks, Sweetness."

"How was Viola killed, Rocky?" I asked.

The Klan killed her and that bastard J. Edgar Hoover ran her name through the mud. Made her out to be a communist, drug addict, and a whore to conceal the fact that an FBI informant was with the Klan when they murdered her." Rocky shook his head. "Last time I saw her we were enjoying cold iced tea in Selma, Alabama on the porch of Mrs. Adela Jefferson. Adela had stories to make you laugh and others to make you cry. On one visit she told Viola and I how she used to help run a medical clinic where a woman could go to have an abortion. She coined a phrase, *None but the Father*. I asked her what it meant and Great Caesar's Ghost, I couldn't believe the answer."

Rocky had my full attention. "What did the phrase mean?"

"Those nuns got pregnant, and it happened after they were raped by a priest, a father, from the local parish. And those nuns couldn't do a damn thing about it. So they took care of things the only way they felt they could."

"Rocky, that's horrible."

"Sure as hell is. That's why I say, just because a man wears the cloth it don't mean a damn thing. There are many good priests, but you're bound to get a rotten apple in the bunch every now and again, just like McCrudden. You know, William Dubin was one of the priests who wanted to pay respect to Viola's memory by having a special mass for her. And for that, McCrudden suspended him from the priesthood."

"I'm anxious to meet your friend."

"Let me give him a call and see if we can pay him a visit tomorrow."

"Perfect."

Chapter 13

NEWS FROM THE MOUNTAIN TOP

On our way to see William Dubin, Rocky told me the former priest had married. I wondered aloud. "Do you think the Church will ever allow priests to marry?"

Rocky laughed, "No possible way. Although I will say, the chance of priests marrying is greater than women gaining entry into the priesthood. The Church is really missing out. Take me for example, I might find myself going to church on a regular basis if I could get on my knees and confess my sins to a woman. Absolution would feel so good."

"You're too much."

"I'm only speaking the truth."

When we reached William Dubin's ranch style home, rows of colored flowers stretched across the front yard. A slight man with a full beard dropped his pruning shears and approached as Rocky's Lincoln came to a stop.

"My dear friend, Rocky, you've arrived at the perfect time of year. The alstromeria, gerbera, and daffodils couldn't be in better display."

"William, it's all quite lovely."

"Flowers, there's not a single bad thing about them. Pure beauty, unlike the man you came here to ask me about."

"William, this is Alejandra, my adopted daughter."

"Pleased to meet you. Rocky filled me in a little. How may I help?"

I dove right in, "Do you recognize the man in this photo?"

I passed the Polaroid to William. He took his time looking at it. "Am I supposed to know him?"

"I was hoping you'd tell me it's Monsignor Crowe."

"I can see a likeness, but I'm not certain. This picture doesn't give me a full frontal view of his face. If it's the Monsignor, he's much younger here."

"What can you tell me about Crowe?"

"He's the Cardinal's finance wizard. He runs the Archdiocese. I didn't have a real association with him other than attending some of the same public services and events."

"If this is Crowe then it's likely he and his boss, Cardinal McCrudden, are involved in a case I'm working on. I don't know how you can help, but we thought if you could tell us more about McCrudden it might shed some light."

"Ah, a fishing expedition. Well, let's see if I can give you something a bit bigger than a morsel of bait on the line."

"Rocky told me the Cardinal pretty much fired you from the priesthood."

"That's about right. The Cardinal grew tired of me. I had been a thorn in his side for some time, and it started with Chávez Ravine. I had been a priest in Chávez Ravine, at *El Santo Niño*. I loved that chapel. When the city decided they were going to tear down people's homes and build a housing project it was devastating, but we held out hope that the new residences would be good for the people in the long run. We had no other choice than to feel optimistic, but that didn't take away the heartbreak of seeing people cheated out of their homes. More tragedy came when the housing project never got built. The Cardinal used his influence to make sure of it."

I pressed, "Did you try to fight him on the housing project?"

"I sure did, but I couldn't match his power. But my battles with the Cardinal didn't begin and end there. Things worsened between us when I learned Walter O'Malley needed one last parcel to secure all the land he needed for his new stadium. Did you know the plot of land where my little church, *El Santo Niño*, used to stand is where the centerfielder, Willie Davis, now catches those high fly balls in Dodger Stadium?"

"I had no idea."

"My heart and *El Santo Niño* were one. When I found out O'Malley needed the *El Santo Niño* land I contacted the Cardinal and pleaded with him not to sell. The Cardinal told me that the Archdiocese no longer owned the land. When I asked him to tell me who did, he said I had no business concerning myself with the fiscal matters of the diocese. At that point I had no other choice but to find out who did own the land. Have you heard of Clay Whitman?"

"No."

"Clay Whitman happens to be one of the biggest developers in Los Angeles. I found that out in 1952 when the Cardinal transferred the title of the *El Santo Niño* land to a holding company that Whitman owned, the Gateway Real Estate Limited Liability Company. From all accounts the Archdiocese didn't receive any money in the deal which seemed strange."

Rocky questioned, "You say 1952, that would be

before Walter O'Malley thought about bringing the Dodgers to Los Angeles?"

William was quick to respond. "Corruption is like devil grass. Its invasive deep roots take hold and strangle everything good around it. I believe the housing project was a front. Sure there may have been a few folks with good intentions who truly thought new housing would be built, but the power brokers, the devil grass, knew all along they would prevail and the Dodgers would leave Brooklyn for Los Angeles."

William couldn't give me answers fast enough. "Okay, but why would McCrudden give Whitman the land for free?"

"I questioned the Cardinal about it, but of course he didn't have an answer. What I did get was the loss of my parish and a reassignment as a hospital chaplain. I had no choice but to drop the issue."

I pressed again. "Do you think McCrudden took part in the backroom deals to get the Dodgers here?"

"Of course I do. The *El Santo Niño* deal proved it to me. Plus, the Cardinal's stance on the proposed new stadium was no secret."

Rocky piped in, "No secret is right, the Cardinal even went on television to endorse the Dodger Stadium ballot referendum."

William concurred, "That's right."

William's story introduced detours I hadn't expected. "I wonder if McCrudden's been involved in ongoing deals with Clay Whitman."

William spoke his thoughts. "It would not surprise me. If I were you, I'd follow the money."

I had one more thing on my mind. "A man by the name of Gary Bell was found dead. I think he was murdered. Before his body was discovered Bell's wife told me he was worried the father and the son would be coming after him. William, are Cardinal McCrudden and Monsignor Crowe ever referred to as the father and son?"

"No. The Father and Son are designations reserved for the Holy Trinity. Together with the Holy Spirit they describe three divine persons in one God. Alejandra, maybe Gary Bell was using a metaphor."

As we made our way back home we passed perfect rows of orange trees, followed by lemon, and then grapefruit. I started to think about how fields are plowed, seeds are sown, fruit is grown, picked, and eaten. If only life were managed like an orchard with clearly defined paths. But life is never a clearly defined path. Five dead bodies in the back of a pickup truck, a cardinal with interests beyond the church, a real estate developer with ties to the Archdiocese, a possible metaphor with no known meaning, all proof that nothing was clear.

Chapter 14

DIRTY MONEY

William Dubin's words, "follow the money," played over and over in my head. For the Los Angeles Archdiocese following the money translated into property. I had no better place to start than the County Clerk's Office where I could request a record for all Archdiocese real estate holdings.

Harriett worked fast to have another one of her contacts ready to help me when I arrived at the Clerk's Office. In quick order Harriett's friend, Shirley, handed me strips of microfilm with the property title data I needed. I scrolled up and down a long list of properties before focusing my attention on the *El Santo Niño* Chapel address. I wanted to verify that McCrudden had indeed turned over the chapel property to Clay Whitman's holding company as William Dubin claimed. When I found the address I saw that, in 1952, a transfer of title from the Roman Catholic Archbishop of Los Angeles to the Housing Authority had indeed occurred. I assumed the transfer change reflected the city's takeover of the property via eminent domain to make way for the proposed federal housing project. If this were the case then William Dubin could have been mistaken about McCrudden having anything to do with the Dodger Stadium deal. I began to think I had hit another dead end when the next entry on the list caught my eye. I saw a similar parcel number indicating it would be in the same map book. The transfer of title occurred in 1952, but this time between the Roman Catholic Archbishop of Los Angeles and the Gateway Real Estate Limited Liability Company. Among shelves of cataloged books I found the one with the parcel map of *El Santo Niño* and adjacent properties. From what I could see McCrudden may not have sold the *El Santo Niño* chapel property, but he did sell a parcel to Gateway that was next door.

"Thought I'd come by and check on you. Harriett asked me to take good care of you. Are you finding everything you need?"

Like Harriett, Shirley was a handsome woman and her bright pink-red lipstick brightened the nondescript work surroundings.

"Thanks, Shirley. I've made some progress, but I'm hoping you can help me with another search. Would it be possible to get the sale history, starting in 1952, for two pieces of property?"

"I can do that, just write down the addresses."

I quickly wrote down the two Chávez Ravine addresses and while I waited for Shirley to return I scanned the list for any other properties with a connection to Gateway. Now that I had something tangible, it took no time to find that needle in a haystack: a single property with a title transfer in 1962 between the Roman Catholic Archbishop of Los Angeles and Gateway. The most interesting thing about the find was that the property was located in the 4000 block of Hammel Street, north of Belvedere Park.

Shirley returned. "Here you go."

I didn't expect to see what Shirley showed me. "Wow, the Archdiocese only received $2800 for the sale of the chapel to the Housing Authority in 1952. I'm confused by what's noted for 1955 though."

"What's noted is a bit of shady history. In 1952 your chapel property became part of a larger 169 acre parcel sold to the Housing Authority for slightly over five million dollars; the Archdiocese received $2800 for its share. This same large parcel that included the chapel site sold again in 1955 to the City of Los Angeles, but this time for just over one million dollars."

"Wait, that doesn't add up."

"You're right. Smells rotten, doesn't it? When the Housing Authority sold the property to the City in 1955 they only recouped about six hundred dollars for their $2800 investment on that chapel property alone. We the tax payers were taken for a ride on that one."

"How was that allowed?"

"If I remember correctly, Congress authorized the Housing Authority to sell the large parcel with the provision that the City use the land for an appropriate public purpose."

"But how could Dodger Stadium be considered a public purpose?"

"Sugar, you're young. Excuse my candor, but there aren't enough orifices in one human body to accommodate all the people who will simultaneously try to screw you over in this life."

"I guess you're right."

"I know I'm right. Take a look at that other property you asked me to check. In 1952, the property was sold to

Gateway for $1000 and then Gateway turns around and sells it to the City in 1955 for one million. That's some kind of property appreciation."

"Now I'm really lost. The chapel property depreciates and this other adjacent property appreciates? It doesn't make sense."

"Sugar, once you add on a few more years to that young life of yours, you won't be surprised by the thievery in this world. Eventually the City deeded your two properties that were part of that large 169 acre parcel to O'Malley in exchange for no money."

"No money?"

"That's right. In fact, the City paid to grade the land and the County paid to create new access roads. For his part, O'Malley consented to build a public park but that never happened. He got away with just building his precious stadium."

"And I suppose O'Malley initially agreed to build the public park to qualify the deal as serving an appropriate public purpose?"

"You're catching on quick. It's easy to see the greed when you start to look."

Chapter 15

PLACE OF FELLOWSHIP

I couldn't sleep. There was no point. In three hours the surgeon would start to cut my *Tía's* flesh. Pieces of breast meat would be sliced and placed in a disposal pan destined for an incinerator. The thought haunted me. By dawn's break I found refuge in my car, *Azulita*. Her cocoon offered me temporary protection from the reality that nothing is permanent. I drove aimlessly until I came to rest across from Our Lady Queen of Angels. Without much thought, I opened the car door and walked into the church. I found the sanctuary empty like the night it offered me refuge when Ashworth's men were bent on finding and killing me.

I took a seat in the front pew. Jesus' near naked body was hanging above the altar nailed to a cross. The glossy statue of his mother, Mary, stood off to the right. Mary did not come to life as she had in a dream during my previous visit, when she told me that political retribution led to her son's crucifixion; his simple message of love and compassion stoked fear in those who held the reins of power. She told me not much had changed since the year 33: the powerful were still manipulating the masses. Mary had pointed to the iconic image of her son nailed to the cross as proof. If the church really cared about spreading His message, a more befitting image would show Him washing the feet of a stranger, she explained. Can you imagine, she had asked, if we all embraced each other with love? I couldn't imagine, but I wanted to.

Even though my brain told me nothing or no one could intervene to keep Carmen alive, I looked up at Jesus wanting to believe in the power of prayer. My reason was simple. I selfishly wanted more time with Carmen before I had to say goodbye.

§§§§§§

When I arrived at the hospital Rocky and Sumire were about to leave.

Rocky whispered, "Hello Sweetheart. She's been asleep since we got here. You just missed Jaime."

"Have you seen the doctor?"

"We did, and he said that she's doing well. He thinks

they were able to get all the cancer and she should be able to go home in a couple of days."

Through tears I cried out "I can't believe it! That's great news, Rocky."

"She's going to be okay. She's not going anywhere, Alejandra."

"Meow."

Bewildered I asked, "Where's that coming from?"

Calmly Sumire answered, "Gato insisted on coming." Sumire opened up her knapsack to reveal the head of her handsome black cat.

"How long are all of you staying?" I asked.

Rocky answered, "We were getting ready to leave. Thought we'd go for an early lunch. Want to join us? There's not much you can do here. She needs her rest. The doctor thinks she'll be asleep most of the day."

"I'll go with you. I haven't eaten yet."

Sumire offered some advice. "The body must be cherished."

After filling up on oil soaked bags of fried shrimp from Johnny's Shrimp Boat at 2nd and Main, I told Rocky about my latest findings.

"Your friend William Dubin was partially right. It looks like McCrudden did sell a property to Clay Whitman, but it wasn't the church property. It was an adjacent parcel. But here's where it gets interesting. McCrudden sold it cheap and after a short time Whitman re-sold it to the City for quite a pretty penny."

"Interesting indeed. If the property was worth what the City paid then why didn't McCrudden want to get more for his Archdiocese?"

"We're on the same page. I found another property that McCrudden sold to Whitman back in 1962. You and Sumire want to go with me to check it out? It's close to Belvedere Park on Hammel Street?"

Sumire answered first. "Gato and me are in."

Rocky followed, "Me, too."

§§§§§§§

We arrived at the address to find a shuttered run-down church. A chain link fence surrounded the property and the only way in was through a padlocked gate.

"Rocky can you work your magic and open this lock?"

"Step aside Sweetheart, I have the perfect tool for the job right here in my wallet."

Rocky pulled out a long and slender metal pick and set to work. After some effort he had us inside the gated yard and then he worked his pick again to get us into the church.

Sumire was the first to comment. "Don't they call this trespassing?"

"Only if we get caught." I responded.

Rocky added his opinion. "By the looks of things there's not much to trespass. This place is a mess."

Statues of saints lay tumbled over and broken on the floor. Church pews were covered with dust and cobwebs hung from the rafters. As we made our way toward the sanctuary a loud screeching whine pierced our ears. It was Gato. Sumire spoke what we all knew. "Gato senses something wrong."

We followed Gato's cry to a small room located off to the side of the altar and found the feline feverishly clawing at a locked door. Rocky set his pick to work. When the door opened we walked onto a small landing overlooking what appeared to be a dark cellar space. Gato immediately sped down a rickety wooden staircase and we followed with trepidation. At the bottom Rocky pulled a long string connected to a light bulb to take us out of the darkness. The light revealed a bed cot and strewn clothes across the floor. Food wrappers, a jug with water, and a bucket with human waste suggested the place had been recently inhabited.

In a whisper Sumire summed up the scene. "This is no place for living."

From across the room Gato screeched again. We followed the sound of his whine to a corner of the room.

Rocky was the first to voice what we all saw. "She's dead. It looks recent."

"How do you know?" I asked.

Rocky shined his pen light on the body. "No bloating, no smell. Look at the wound where that thin blade is sticking through her chest. The edges are still swollen and red. The war taught me more than I wanted to know about death."

I didn't waste any time. "I'm going to call the police."

Within minutes of placing the call a law enforcement team arrived and an hour later Lt. Smitz and Detective Carr showed up on the scene.

Smitz spotted me and walked over while Detective

Carr passed me as if I didn't exist. "Alejandra Marisol, why am I not surprised? I understand you told dispatch this scene is related to the Belvedere Park murders. What have you found?"

"The scene will speak for itself, Lieutenant."

"Not even going to give me a preview?"

"One dead woman. Looks like she died from a stab wound."

"Quite a find. And how did you come onto this place?"

"Well, that's a long story."

"Of course it is. I've got time to listen, but I guess the person you need to tell is Carr."

Smitz walked toward Carr and motioned for me to follow. "Detective, I'm sure you'll find what Alejandra has to say informative."

Detective Carr snapped back, "Really, Lieutenant?"

"Yes, really. I will pull rank this time."

Detective Carr relented and slowly walked over to me. "Okay, what can you tell me?"

"First, you need to get in touch with the person who owns this place."

"I've already spoken to Mr. Whitman."

"What did he say?"

"He's on his way down here. He sounded pretty shocked when I told him what you reported."

"Seems interesting that you'd call him before investigating the scene for yourself. Why would you take my report over the phone seriously?"

"Is there some reason I should think you'd lie?"

"No."

"Good. After finding out Whitman owned this place, I called him because I like efficiency. I like to get my cases cleared quickly."

I countered, "I think this case is going to be an exception. The scene you'll find in the cellar is tied to the Belvedere Park murders."

"Unless you have concrete evidence I'll be the judge of that. Tell me, Miss Marisol, how did you find this place?"

"I found it by making a connection to the previous owner of this place, the Catholic Archdiocese."

Carr laughed, "Let me guess, next thing you're going to tell me is that a priest committed the murder. No, no, how about a nun?"

"Look, I'm here, aren't I? It might be worthwhile to

question Whitman and Cardinal McCrudden about their financial relationship."

"Because you think a financial transaction leads to the formation of a murderous partnership? You're really grasping."

"You don't even think it's worth investigating?"

"I live in a world of facts, not make believe."

"This isn't make believe."

"I'm sure once Whitman gets here we'll have some answers."

Carr turned away from me and toward a patrol officer who tapped him on his shoulder. "Detective, Clay Whitman is here to see you."

"Show him over."

Clay Whitman wore his wealth. Dressed in a three-piece suit and sporting a gold ring with a nugget large enough to choke on, he took long confident strides toward us.

"Hello, Detective. Clay Whitman at your service. I got here as soon as I could. What you briefly told me sounds absolutely horrible. Are there any new details?"

"The investigation is really just starting. In fact, I

have yet to see the scene. Miss Marisol with the *LA Times* is the one who made the discovery."

Whitman turned toward me. He looked at me through cold blue-grey eyes as if he knew me. "Miss Marisol, let me take the liberty of thanking you for your efforts here today. I think it goes without saying that if you hadn't made this discovery the poor soul found here would not have been given a respectful resting place. But I must ask, do you make it a habit of trespassing onto other people's property?"

"No, I don't Mr. Whitman."

"Good to know. Given the good work Miss Marisol has done here today I assume we can forego pressing any charges. Is that correct, Detective?"

"Yes, Mr. Whitman. Thank you for your under-standing. I am sure Miss Marisol is quite contrite. Isn't that right, Miss Marisol?"

I couldn't believe what I was hearing, but I had to agree . "Yes, that's right."

Detective Carr wasn't finished. "Good. Now if you will please excuse us."

I was furious, but there was nothing I could do. I turned to walk away but I moved slowly straining to hear the conversation between Carr and Whitman.

"So, Mr. Whitman, what can you tell me about this building?"

"I purchased this place about ten years ago. I had plans to tear down the church and construct an apartment building, but I haven't gotten around to it."

Carr noticed I hadn't taken my leave. He shot a smug look my way and walked Whitman in the opposite direction. For now I'd go quietly.

Chapter 16

POWERS THAT BE

The dank hot air focused my mind on images I didn't want to recall: the truck bed, the church cellar. I tried to focus on my driving but a wave of panic began to settle in my chest. The weight of my anxiety pulled tears from my eyes. It felt as if I were falling into quicksand. I took my eyes away from the road and wished I could stop time and melt into the sky's blue. Without warning my torso slammed up against my steering wheel as *Azulita* hit a curb. In one frantic motion I jerked the wheel to the left to pull back onto the street, but I over compensated and cut off the Helm's Bakery truck following close behind. The truck's back hatch flew open throwing trays of fresh baked goods into the air as the driver swerved and barely missed me. I pulled over and sat for a moment to settle down. I had nearly caused a serious accident as evidenced by the raspberry jelly donut splattered across my windshield. Even so, I was grateful for the distraction. It had calmed the pain. I merged back onto Broadway and continued toward the *Times* Building.

When I took my seat across from Harriett she wasted little time telling me the bad news. "I have to take you off the story. I should have never let you take the lead in the first place. I should have assigned our crime reporters to cover the Belvedere Park murders."

"But Harriett, I know the players. I know the back story here."

"I know."

"Why are you doing this?"

"I don't have a choice. This is coming from the top. Looks like a complaint has been brought against you. You trespassed onto private property."

"If I hadn't that latest victim would have never been discovered."

"Damn it, I don't have a choice. This is coming down from the top, the publisher, as in Otis Chandler. He doesn't like his reporters breaking the law for their stories. I warned you."

"You mean he doesn't like it when they get caught."

"You're right. Look, you should have called in your discovery of the body as an anonymous tip. Experience with this kind of thing would have taught you that much."

"This must be Clay Whitman's doing. He wants me off the case. Your friend at the County Clerk's Office helped me locate documents showing that McCrudden sold two pieces of property to Whitman. One located in Chávez Ravine and the other where we found that woman's body on Hammel Street."

"Damn, damn, damn." Harriett shook her head and looked at me stunned.

"Now it looks like we have a Cardinal and a rich developer potentially involved in a sex ring and murder. The pieces are here. I can't give up on this now."

"You're right, we've come too far to give into pressure."

I remembered my final question for William Dubin and asked a similar one. "Harriett, does Clay Whitman have a son?"

"That's a question out of left field. Why do you ask?"

"Gary Bell told his wife he was afraid the father and the son would be coming after him. I'm wondering if Bell was referring to Clay Whitman and his son."

"He used to have a son, a younger daughter too. Both were killed in a house fire when they were young."

"Harriett, how long ago?"

"About twenty years ago. It was tragic. It was in the news for days. I even remember the children's names, Robert and Roberta."

"I wish I knew what the father and the son meant to Gary Bell."

Harriett lit a cigarette. "I don't know, but first things first. Here's how we'll play it from here on out. Officially you'll be off the Belvedere Park story. I'll pass it off to someone else in Crime. I'll make sure they focus on the heinous nature of the murders, nothing more."

"What about Chandler? I don't want your job jeopardized."

"I'll take care of myself."

"Okay, I'll be in touch."

Chapter 17

IF AT FIRST YOU DON'T SUCCEED,

TRY AGAIN

"Anything yet? Can you tell me anything about the woman found in the church cellar?"

"Interesting case. Come over."

Armand lifted the sheet to reveal the young corpse. She looked about my age, somewhere in her early twenties. Beyond the residual dirt that framed the outline of her cheeks and chin I saw a beautiful woman who even in death held my gaze as my eyes traced her soft brown skin.

Armand's voice jolted me back to the cutting reality that I wasn't standing at the foot of this woman's bed watching her sleep. I was looking at a murder victim, afforded no dignity, as she lay naked on a cold stainless steel table.

"Look right here. A thin blade was thrust under the xiphoid process at the bottom edge of the sternum. The person knew what he was doing because the blade was angled perfectly to pierce the heart. But that's not what makes the case interesting. Someone tried to kill her before she was stabbed to death."

"Huh?"

"I found a large concentration of a tocolytic drug in her system."

"What's that?"

"It suppresses contractions and that's why there was a large piece of the placenta still in her uterus."

"She was pregnant?"

"Yep, and I'd wager that the tocolytic was injected after she gave birth keeping the placenta from being fully released."

"How can you die from that?"

"If the placenta isn't completely discharged from the uterus the blood vessels inside continue to bleed and you hemorrhage to death. For some reason the drug didn't take full effect. Whoever killed her wasn't successful the first time and had to resort to another method."

"So where's the baby?"

"Maybe born dead or murdered too."

"We didn't find a dead baby. What if the baby was taken alive?"

Armand questioned, "But why would a killer want to deal with a live baby?"

"They'd deal with a live baby if it's seen as a commodity."

"What are you saying, Alejandra?"

"I think you know. It's too damn horrifying to speak out loud. It would be a perfect operation. There wouldn't be any need to try and coax a kid for your pleasure. You wouldn't have to run the risk of being caught kidnapping a child. You'd have a supply of anonymous babies. Babies that don't exist and can be easily disposed."

"And you think there are enough demons in this world to make such an operation worthwhile?"

"You know that best of all. You see the horrors, firsthand, right in this room."

"Well sure, but this is a whole other thing. It's sickening beyond belief and I sure hope there's some other explanation."

"Armand, what other explanation?"

"I don't know, but your idea is too unbelievable."

"I really hope you're right. Before I leave I'll need you to take a picture of this victim for me. It may come in handy."

Suddenly Olivia's voice boomed across the room. "*Primo*, I'm here."

Armand responded. "This is a surprise, I didn't expect you until later."

"I have a long incubation going for an experiment I'm running so I thought I'd come a little earlier."

"I have the blood sample on this latest female victim."

"Very good, *Primo*. I expect to have the DNA fingerprinting results completed on your first five victims, and this new one, within a day."

Olivia turned toward me. "Hello, Alejandra. Good to see you again."

"Nice to see you too. I hope your results will bring us closer to solving this case."

"More data can't hurt."

I questioned Olivia's words. Her previous results had hurt. Her data had brought us to see the vulnerability and innocence behind the faces of the men found slaughtered in the back of a truck. I now wondered what her new revelations would force me to see and endure.

Chapter 18

SAINT BASIL'S

Católicos Por La Raza, a coalition of Mexican-American Catholics, saw Saint Basil's Catholic Church as a gift to the affluent and a symbol of disregard for the poor. They couldn't reconcile constructing such an opulent structure at the cost of three million dollars while the Church did little to alleviate the plight of many who lived in substandard conditions.

This was my first visit, standing where *Católicos Por La Raza* had called on their sympathizers to gather for Midnight Mass on December 24th, 1969. The events of the evening didn't go well as more than 200 organized demonstrators pushed their way inside to chastise the Church. Cardinal McCrudden had begun the Christmas service when security officers, who were later joined by police, quelled the disturbance and returned order, but only after several protesters had been arrested.

Now here almost two years later, I recalled how McCrudden compared the protesters to the "rabble that gathered at the foot of the Cross when Christ died." Although I wasn't here to protest construction of a contemporary façade, I was here to see beyond the veneer. I needed answers that weren't visible from the outside.

As I gathered the nerve to knock on Saint Basil's rectory door Monsignor Crowe emerged. Before he could take a seat in his four door beige sedan I called out to him. "Monsignor, do you have a moment?"

Monsignor Crowe turned around to see me. Our eyes locked and I knew beyond any doubt he was the man in the Polaroid.

"Excuse me, do we know each other?"

"No Monsignor, we've never met. My name is Alejandra Marisol, I'm a reporter with the *Times*."

"What can I do for you?"

"We came across a photo we'd like to ask you about."

I wasn't about to show Crowe the photo for fear he'd take it from me and destroy it. Instead, I let a pointed description do the work. "It's a black and white Polaroid. It shows you on top of a woman. You're both naked. The woman's hands are tied to the bed frame."

Crowe was taken aback. His cheeks flushed and his eyes widened. He stood quiet but quickly regained his footing. It was obvious he didn't find himself on the defensive very often. He took aim and fired. "No such photo exists, not one with me in it."

I pushed back. "There's no mistake, it's you all right. Any comment before publication?"

"It isn't me and I'll deny it. Now if you'll excuse me, I have an important meeting to attend."

Crowe wasted little time driving away leaving me with nothing. I started to head back to my car when I noticed a gardener alongside the rectory cutting back the shrubbery. It was a long shot but worth pursuing.

"Hello, Sir."

"Yes."

"I have an appointment to meet the Monsignor."

"The Monsignor left. I don't know when he'll be back."

"Oh my, I'm sure he told me to be here at this time. I wonder if I got it wrong and I'm supposed to meet him somewhere else. Do you know where he went?"

"He has a lunch meeting every Wednesday at Clifton's."

"Can you tell me your name?"

"Romero."

"Romero, maybe you can help?"

Romero shot an affable look my way. "How?"

"I'm a social worker for a hospital. The large one close to downtown, LA County General."

"Yes, I know it."

"Over the phone I told the Monsignor I needed to find anyone who might know a woman admitted to the hospital. She arrived very sick and before she became unconscious she mentioned the Monsignor's name and Saint Basil's."

I passed the picture Armand took of the dead woman over to Romero. "Do you know her?"

"Itzel, that's her name. Will she be okay? She doesn't look good."

Romero was visibly upset, but I couldn't turn back now. I had the opening I needed. "Yes, we think she'll be okay. Can you tell me anything about her? Where we might be able to find her family?"

"She worked and lived here, but only for a little while. One day Monsignor took her away and she never came back."

144

"How long ago?"

"About a month."

"Do you know where the Monsignor took her?"

"I guess to a place to have her baby."

"She was pregnant?"

"Yes."

"Did she ever talk about the father of the baby?"

"No, but the Monsignor took care of her. He's a good man. He helps women like Itzel."

"And does the Monsignor always take the women away before they have their babies?"

"Yes, to a home for pregnant women."

"Do any of the women ever come back here?"

"No."

"Do you know where they go after they have their babies?"

"I think the Monsignor helps them get back to their families in Mexico."

Cynically, I asked, "Is that what the Monsignor told you?"

Romero's puzzled face told me I had overstepped. I quickly backtracked. "I meant to say how nice of the Monsignor to do that. I'm hoping the Monsignor will be

145

able to help us find Itzel's family."

"You'll have to ask the Monsignor. I don't know."

"Is there anyone else who knew Itzel?"

"Lupe spent a little time with her. I'll take you to her."

Romero led me to the back of the rectory where we found two women preparing food in a large open kitchen. He walked over to the woman dicing onions. Of the two, she was the oldest and clearly not pregnant like her cooking partner who was busy stirring the contents of a large pot.

Romero called out to Lupe. "*Hola Lupe, esta señorita dice que tiene preguntas sobre Itzel y su familia. Ella dice que Itzel está en el hospital.*"

Even after hearing Itzel was in the hospital and that I came to see if she had family, Lupe stayed focused on her onions and kept her response to a few words. "*No tengo nada que decir.*"

She said she had nothing to say but I made another attempt, pleading directly with Lupe to tell me something about Itzel. "*¿Lupe, por favor, qué sabes de Itzel?*"

Lupe didn't budge. She shook her head and said nothing. I turned to the young pregnant woman in the room and asked if she knew Itzel. "*¿La conoces?*"

I could barely hear her response. "No."

Romero voiced the obvious. "We can't help you. Itzel wasn't here long."

I felt like the young woman was hiding something, but I didn't push. "Thanks for trying to help."

Before leaving I asked Romero to confirm that the number I had for the rectory was the best way to follow up with the Monsignor. After saying the Edison exchange Romero recited the numbers I used to reach St. Basil's. It was music to my ears and it cemented Eduardo Cuevas' connection to this place.

"Sure do love it when people use the phone exchanges." I said.

Romero added, "The Monsignor loves them too. He uses them all the time."

As Romero ushered me to the front door I could hear Lupe's words. "*Graciela, ve a la tienda y compra pan, del que le gusta al Monseñor.*" Lupe had asked Graciela to buy the Monsignor's favorite bread. I saw the request as my chance. I'd wait on the street for Graciela to return from the store and try my luck one more time. Eduardo Cuevas managed to leave the clue that brought me here, now I hoped mentioning his name to Graciela could bring me more.

I stood at the corner of Kingsley Drive and Wilshire Boulevard and waited. When I spotted Graciela I walked to meet her before she could turn into the rectory. I got ready to pull Eduardo Cuevas, literally, from my pocket. I handed Graciela the morgue photo of Eduardo Cuevas. "*¿Lo conoces?* Do you know him?"

The woman stared at the photo and remained silent. I pushed again. "*Por favor, si lo conoces, dime.* Please tell me if you know him."

Graciela shied away from me and didn't say a word.

I had to take a harder line. I told her to take a good look at the picture to see that Eduardo was dead. That he was murdered. I told her I had lied at the rectory. Itzel had also been murdered and that she would be next if she refused to talk to me.

I asked again, "*¿Conoces a* Eduardo Cuevas?"

Graciela stared at the ground while answering. "*Sí, lo conozco, pero no sabía su nombre.*" She'd seen him she said, but she didn't know his name.

How did she know him? "*¿Cómo lo conociste?*"

The young woman cried as she answered. "*Necesitaba dinero y una amiga me exigió hablar con él.*"

Graciela needed money and a friend told her to see Eduardo. I couldn't help but think the worst. I expected an answer I didn't want to hear. Regardless, I had to ask what kind of deal Eduardo made with Graciela. "*¿Qué es lo que tenías que hacer?*"

"*Tener un bebé.*"

Graciela had confirmed my fear. She would be paid to have a baby, but for whom? "*¿Y, para quién vas a tener el bebé?*"

"*Para una pareja que no puede tener su propio bebé.*"

Graciela's answer didn't align with the perverted and deranged path I had shared with Armand about Itzel. Even though I had heard of people being paid to have babies for infertile couples, I wasn't buying it, not in this case. Everything about Graciela's face indicated she believed what she told me. But if it were as simple as exchanging money for a baby then Itzel should still be alive. There had to be something else going on. Before leaving I had to confirm my suspicion and ask who fathered her baby? "*¿Quién es el padre de su bebé?*"

I handed her the photos of the four young men found murdered along with Eduardo Cuevas. Graciela pointed to one of them and began to sob. She told me she didn't know him but he treated her well. They each wanted the same thing: a better life for themselves and their families back in Mexico.

I asked one last question. "*¿El Monseñor te ha lastimado?*"

This time she looked me straight in the eye and answered in the few English words she could string together. "No hurt. *El Monseñor*, he a good man."

Chapter 19

JUST A PILE OF CRAP

The phone was ringing when I walked into my house. As soon as I answered Armand began to tell me about Olivia's DNA test results. I couldn't believe none of the five murdered men fathered Itzel's baby. If I assumed Graciela told me the truth about one of the murdered men fathering her child, then who had fathered Itzel's? With no one else to accuse I placed my bet on Monsignor Crowe. Even though I knew little about DNA testing, I was certain that a sample of the Monsignor's cells was needed.

The gardener, Romero, mentioned Crowe had a lunch date at Clifton's and that's where I needed to go. I wouldn't be able to approach Crowe though, not after our interaction. As luck would have it Rocky and Sumire were home and on board to help me get my sample.

On our way downtown Rocky offered up an idea. "Sumire and Gato will distract the Monsignor while I pickpocket him. I'll make sure to get something that'll have his cells, like a comb or handkerchief. What do you think?"

Sumire enthusiastically agreed to the plan. "Gato and I are ready."

"Here's a picture of him so you'll know what he looks like." I showed Rocky and Sumire the same recent article with Crowe's picture I had shown Harriett. "Once Sumire confirms Crowe is still inside, you'll both wait for him outside the restaurant. I'll park ahead. One last thing, make sure whatever you take from him gets placed in here."

I handed Rocky a small plastic bag. "We need a clean sample, one with only Crowe's cells. We have to limit the chance of any contaminating DNA from you and Sumire."

"Not my place to question." Rocky said.

I turned to Sumire. "How will you distract the Monsignor?"

Rocky interrupted to answer. "Shit out of luck."

"You're saying Sumire won't be able to distract him?" I asked.

"Shit out of luck. That's what I call my petrified poop." Rocky opened a paper bag to show us the contents.

"That's disgusting. Where did you get it and why do you still have it?"

"World War I. It's my good luck charm."

I shook my head. "I'd love to hear this one but right now we have to get going. Rocky, promise you'll tell me the story later."

"It's a promise."

I turned to Sumire. "How are you planning to use the poop?"

"I'll place it on the sidewalk and ask the Monsignor to hold Gato so I can clean it up."

I questioned the logic in her plan. "If you're planning to pretend this pile came from Gato there's no way Crowe will buy it. It's too big."

Sumire countered, "Won't matter. You'll see."

"Alejandra, I got to agree with Sumire. I'll get what I need before Crowe even realizes the pile can't possibly be Gato's. Remember, this is my lucky shit."

After Sumire confirmed Crowe was inside Clifton's, she placed the poop pile on the sidewalk. When Crowe exited the restaurant Sumire walked toward him with a leashed Gato at her side. I could hear the conversation from where I was parked. "Father, please can you help? Can you hold my cat? He couldn't wait."

Sumire pointed to the large mound on the ground.

Crowe paused and looked down. "That came from your cat?"

Before Sumire could muster an answer Rocky had brushed by the priest and kept walking ahead. From what I saw there was no way Rocky could get a sample from Crowe.

"My cat eats like a lion and poops like one too." Sumire announced.

Crowe took ahold of Gato's leash while Sumire scooped up the poop back into the brown paper bag. "Thank you very much, Father."

Once everyone made it back inside the car Rocky gave us the news. "Snatching the Padre's comb couldn't have been easier. And my petrified poop helped get the job done."

"So tell me, Rocky, how did you come across the poop?" I asked.

"We were involved in a large offensive in the Argonne Forest of France, close to the German border. We lost a lot of men there and I came damn close to being one of them. We were out of ammunition and surrounded on all sides. The only thing we could do was to build shallow bunkers, cover them with branches, hide there, and hope the Germans wouldn't see us. When the Germans came rolling through they noticed the misplaced branches covering up some of the bunkers. They shot through the branches and that's when I could hear my comrades screaming before they died."

"They didn't find your bunker?" I asked.

"They would have if it hadn't been for the wild boar that came out of nowhere. He walked right up to the edge of my bunker and stuck his large snout through some of the branches to look right at me. He must have weighed 500 pounds, maybe more. He stayed right there at the edge while the Germans advanced. Even with gunfire everywhere that boar didn't move. When the Germans got to the edge of my bunker they were so focused on that giant boar they missed my hiding place. I stayed in that bunker for a full day waiting for the Germans to clear the area. When I finally climbed out I found out why the boar didn't care about the German advance. He had been busy taking the biggest dump of shit, right there at the edge of my bunker. Just a couple feet away he lay dead. He paid the price for nature calling on him at such a bad time. No doubt about it. I got this shit out of luck and it saved my life. The combination of the light rain during the night and the gunpowder in the air managed to petrify it. So I took a pile as my charm and I've had it ever since."

I shook my head. "That's one crazy story."

Rocky looked down at the pile of petrified organic matter. "War's not pretty and this pile reminds me that nothing but shit comes from it."

"Let's drop off the comb with Armand so he can give it to his cousin for testing and then reward ourselves with a visit to see Carmen." I announced.

We took Gato's high pitched meow as a firm approval of the plan.

Chapter 20

BAIT AND HOOK

"I'm below 200, *M'ija*. Now that Ta is gone I'm seven pounds lighter. Proof you can find something good in almost anything."

"I'm just glad you're going to be okay, *Tía*."

"Doctor says I should be able to go home tomorrow."

Sumire couldn't keep her surprise a secret any longer. "I made new bras, special for you."

Carmen was thrilled. "I can't wait to see them. They're for the new one breasted me?"

"Yes, special for you." Sumire confirmed.

I added more details about Sumire's bra design. "Each bra has one falsie."

"I love it. A prosthetic boob to go with my prosthetic leg. So tell me, how have you all been since I've been laid up in here?"

I answered. "Still trying to get a break in the case. Rocky and Sumire have been a big help."

"Wish I could help you too."

"I know you do, *Tía*."

"What do you know so far, *M'ija*?"

"One thing I'm pretty certain about, I think Cardinal McCrudden is somehow involved."

"Oh *M'ija*, that's too much. Give me the scoop."

"Remember the phone number I dialed using the exchange?"

"Sure, the number was disconnected."

"That's because one of my numbers was wrong. When I redialed using the right number I reached St. Basil's rectory. The Cardinal's right-hand man, Monsignor Crowe, lives there. He's the man in a photo I found at Ashworth's house. Crowe is having sex with a woman tied to a bed in that photo, and I think the Cardinal was blackmailed to keep the photo from going public."

"Shit. The Cardinal? Then it's more like Holy Shit, right *M'ija*?"

"You have a point," I said. "I just know that photo is tied to the victims found at Belvedere Park and to Ashworth's child sex trade."

"What are you going to do now, *M'ija*?"

"I'm not sure. It's not like I can call the Cardinal and

ask him if he was blackmailed."

"Why not? Go ahead and call him on the phone. What's the worst that can happen? He hangs up on you?"

Rocky agreed. "Men with power don't reveal their hand so easily; hanging up would show he's rattled. He won't do that."

"Okay, I'll play it your way. Rocky, do you think your friend William Dubin can get me the Cardinal's phone number?"

"I'm sure of it. I'll call him right now."

I followed Rocky to the public pay phone in the hall. After he got me the Cardinal's number I placed the call and the line connected. "His Eminence, Cardinal McCrudden's residence."

"Good afternoon, my name is Alejandra Marisol. I'm calling from the *LA Times*. I'm hoping to get a comment from the Cardinal regarding a story related to the Archdiocese I'm preparing to write."

"A story regarding what, specifically?"

"It's a sensitive issue so I'd like to speak with the Cardinal directly about it."

"Your name again?"

"Alejandra Marisol."

"One moment."

My heart pounded with nervous anticipation but it didn't have to wait long. "Cardinal McCrudden speaking."

"Thank you, Cardinal, for taking my call. My name is Alejandra Marisol. I'm a reporter with the *LA Times*."

"Yes, how can I help you?"

I didn't beat around the bush. "We've come across a photograph showing Monsignor Crowe in a compromising situation."

"Compromising in what way?"

"The photo is of a sexual nature. Before we go public we're asking for you to comment."

"I'm not making any comment about a photograph you have not shown me."

"So you're not surprised that a photo like the one I've described exists."

I had stoked the embers. "What are you trying to do? How dare you twist my words? Is the *Times* now nothing more than a cheap tabloid?"

I couldn't wait. I had to feed him a larger piece of bait while I had him on the phone. "It's not just the photograph.

We have evidence Monsignor Crowe is involved in a sex trade operation."

"I don't know who's feeding you these lies, but if you print one word of it I'll hold you liable."

He was calling my bluff. "That's fine, Cardinal. I hoped you'd speak to me before the evidence is turned over to the police."

"I want to see this evidence before I say anything."

"When and where?"

"There will be a gala fundraiser for the Archdiocese tonight at the Biltmore Hotel. You can meet me there."

"Not sure that's such a good idea. There will be a lot of people, including the Monsignor I assume."

"Monsignor Crowe will not attend. We'll have our privacy. I'll have meetings with donors throughout the night in a hotel room I have reserved. You can be my last appointment at 11:00pm."

"That will be fine."

"Very well. I'll be in room 916."

Chapter 21

GEISHA SLEUTH

My first challenge, what to wear? I stood in front of my modest closet to see a single dress. It was the one I wore to my mom's funeral. I couldn't bear to wear it again. On the off chance Sumire had something I could borrow, I headed across the path to her unit. As I approached I found her rolled out on an exercise mat.

"Sumire, what are you up to?"

"Getting ready for my Jujutsu martial art meet next week. I'm practicing moves."

"I hate to bother you, but I'm hoping you might have something on the fancy side I can wear tonight."

"Fancy, no. I have nothing like that." Sumire paused. "Wait, maybe I have something. Follow me."

From the back of her closet Sumire brought out a large box. "I think this could work."

Sumire opened the box to reveal a black kimono with large red and white flowers. While the garment was beautiful, it didn't fit what I had in mind. "Uh thanks, but this is too nice for me to wear."

"Please, you take it. It belonged to my mother. If she were alive she would want you to wear it."

I didn't want to hurt Sumire's feelings, but I had to say it. "This style isn't right for me."

Sumire wouldn't take no for an answer. "I will fix it. It won't take long."

Sumire reached back into her closet and this time pulled out her sewing machine. She could see the concern on my face. "Don't worry, it will look good. I'm going to make it fit the times. You can help."

For the next hour I cut fabric as Sumire threaded her bobbin and stitched new seams. When finished she had created what she described as a mini midi. The asymmetrical pattern boasted a formfitting mini skirt on one side and a draping midi that flared just above the knee on the other. The waistline and sleeves of the kimono were drawn in tight for a tapered look.

"It's ready for you to try."

I put it on and loved it. I felt chic and elegant. "Sumire, what do you think about shoes?"

"Knee-high black boots. Where are you going?"

"I need to meet a priest, a high ranking one. He's hiding something and I need to find out what it is."

"Truth doesn't stay hidden. Like a white grub hatched from a buried egg; it eventually worms its way above ground."

"I hope the truth makes it to the surface before someone tries to bury me."

"You shouldn't go alone. I will come with you."

"Thanks, Sumire, but an LAPD captain is going to meet me there. He'll make sure I stay safe."

"Good."

§§§§§§§

I had never seen anything like the Biltmore Hotel. Frescos, murals, embroidered tapestries, and other wondrous treasures were everywhere I turned. The closest I'd ever gotten to this kind of posh elegance was when my mom took me "play shopping," as she called it. One of our favorite destinations was Bullock's Department Store. Its white marbled walls and ornate deco design would transport me into a world of pageantry. I saw nothing imaginary about my world right now. Everything in my sight was real, including the tall commanding figure who brushed by me dressed in a cassock that reached to the ground. It was Cardinal McCrudden and he walked with a confidence I imagined only came from thinking you had a direct connection to God.

I followed him from a safe distance into the Crystal Ballroom. The palatial space boasted an arcade of arched windows that were outlined with lush baroque draperies. Sconces anchored onto columns bounced ambient lighting off the walls and overhead chandeliers eliminated any shadows where I could hide. My outfit had caught the attention of several in attendance, one of whom walked toward me.

"Mr. Whitman."

"Ah, Miss Marisol. You're the last person I expected to see."

"I could say the same thing about you."

"I happen to be a big supporter of the Cardinal's. He has a real vision, not only for knowing what's needed to prepare our soul for salvation, but also for the political structure that's needed to feed and sustain the Church."

"Interesting perspective. Somehow I didn't take you for a man of God."

"God lives in us all. So tell me, Miss Marisol, what brings you to the Biltmore? I trust they let you in the door and you didn't have to break in. Are you here looking for a dead body? Under the table perhaps?"

"Don't you care about the murdered woman found on your property?"

"Oh, I care immensely. I also care about the sanctity of property rights."

"You talk about your property as if its worth were equal to a human life."

"I'm sorry about the woman who was found dead, and I'm sure Detective Carr will find who's responsible."

"You made sure I'm no longer involved."

"I made a call to an old friend about your misconduct, and he, not I, took you off the story."

"It appears you have a lot of important friends such as Cardinal McCrudden and Otis Chandler. I'm sure the list is quite long."

"Friends are always an important resource. One should not take them for granted. You never know when you might need to call on one for help. Take you and me for example."

I couldn't believe what I heard. "You and I. Are we friends?"

"We could be. The circumstances of how we met were, I admit, a bit strained. I don't like to ever give up on an opportunity to make a new friend."

Clay Whitman pulled out a business card from his jacket pocket and handed it to me. "Should you ever find yourself jobless you may need me. I employ a large number of women like you who were born to clean the mess others leave behind."

I wanted to spit on his card and throw it in his face. "Men like you are blinded by your own power. You won't be prepared for what's coming."

"What could you possibly be talking about?"

"The wretched of the earth, Mr. Whitman. Those you have exploited and manipulated. When they realize their power and take you down. It won't be pretty. It will be downright ugly."

I didn't wait for Clay Whitman to respond. I went to the bar and ordered a shot of Crown Royal on the rocks.

Halfway through my drink my rage started to subside. It was 10:30, and I expected Captain Allen to arrive at any moment. I lifted my glass to take another drink when I felt someone slide into the empty seat next to me. Before I could turn to see who it was, a man's voice offered up an apology. "I'm sorry you had to experience that."

I rotated to see the man now sitting to my left. His chiseled good looks and seductive smile sent an involuntary ripple through my body. I chalked it up to the alcohol and responded by tightly crossing my legs, hoping to quash the wave of arousal. He continued. "I overheard a little bit of that conversation back there. Mr. Whitman can be a bastard." The man took a sip of his drink. "How rude of me to interrupt you and not introduce myself. I'm Bob Dennon and you are?"

With my composure slightly regained, I replied. "Alejandra Marisol."

"Can I get you another drink?"

"Still working on this one, but thank you."

"What brings you here tonight? You don't fit the profile of the typical Archdiocese supporter."

"How's that?"

The slur in Bob Dennon's voice told me the alcohol in his blood had loosened his inhibitions. "Take a look around. Do you see any other women that even remotely look like you?"

I was taken aback. The look of incredulity upon my face couldn't be missed.

Bob Dennon chuckled and his mouth broke into a wide smile. "I only mean that in the most complimentary way. Look at these stodgy women. The stoles they're wearing look more alive than they do. Allow me to say that dress fits you quite nicely."

I relented. "I accept the compliment. And you're right. I'm not here to help the Archdiocese raise money. I'm here working for the *Times*."

"A reporter? Is that how you met Mr. Whitman, covering a story?"

"I guess you could say that. How do you know him?"

"One of his henchmen. There are a few like me here tonight. We look for investors for capital projects that Mr. Whitman's company oversees."

"And the Archdiocese is involved in some of these projects?"

"It's no secret. Mr. Whitman and the Archdiocese have a good working relationship."

"Relationship, is that what it's called?"

"Let's just say Mr. Whitman has his hands in a lot of different deals and the Archdiocese is one of them."

Bob Dennon turned toward the center of the ballroom and then continued. "All these rich people are aching to dole out their money, especially when they know their investments will get them even more cash in the end."

Bob Dennon had my full attention. "How does investing in the Archdiocese make money?"

"I'm not at liberty to discuss financial strategies. Suffice it to say that wealth begets wealth."

"So it literally does pay to have a powerful friend like the Cardinal?"

"Yes. Friends like the Cardinal and his ruthless sidekick, Monsignor Crowe, are good to have."

Bob Dennon mentioned the name of the man I wanted to know more about. "Should I assume you don't like the Monsignor?"

Bob Dennon moved in closer and whispered. "I like you. Can I tell you something, just between you and me?"

170

I didn't know where Bob Dennon was going. "Of course."

"One has to be ruthless when it comes to making money. I don't fault the Monsignor for that. But there is something not right about him."

I wanted to ask Bob Dennon if he thought Crowe could be capable of impregnating women, murdering them, and selling their babies. "What do you mean, not right?"

"Don't listen to me, I've had too much to drink. What do you say we get out of here and go some place where we can get a decent meal? I sure could use a good martini and a steak. Have you ever been to the Pacific Dining Car on 6th?"

"Thanks, but I need to stay. I'm scheduled to meet the Cardinal."

"Face to face with the man of the hour. Well, I hope you get what you need from him. It was nice meeting you. I have a feeling we'll cross paths again. I look forward to seeing you then."

"You're a bit presumptuous, Mr. Dennon."

"Oh please, we've shared time over a drink. First

names from here on out, Alejandra."

"Okay. Nice to meet you, Bob."

Bob left me as I finished my last sip of courage now coating two melting ice cubes at the bottom of my glass. Captain Allen was nowhere in sight. With or without him the time had come to meet the Cardinal for a high stakes winner take all game, and I was ready to play my best poker yet.

§§§§§§

When I exited the elevator on the 9th floor there was no one in sight. I took a slow deliberate walk to my destination, Room 916. I knocked. The door slowly opened and I stepped inside. McCrudden closed the door behind me.

"You're on time. Please have a seat, Miss Marisol."

I took a seat at a small table near the window and Cardinal McCrudden sat across from me. Without any prompting, McCrudden spoke first. "When I arrived in Los Angeles in 1948 to head this great diocese I saw the city before me like an open landscape. I immediately set to work erecting new parishes and schools; each built with the purpose of giving glory to our Almighty Father in Heaven. It is a legacy I am proud to honor with my continued service to God and his people." The Cardinal reached for his crucifix. "I know about the picture you are here to show me. Monsignor Crowe's indiscretion has weighed on my soul for a long time, but he has found his way back to the Lord. His early stumble is far behind him. We all falter, Miss Marisol. This is the reason I have stood by Monsignor Crowe and will continue to do so. He is a good man."

"That's the second time I've heard Monsignor Crowe referred to as a good man, but do good men prey on the weaknesses of immigrants? Do good men sell children for sex?"

"You're like a cannon without a cannonball, Miss Marisol. You might be able to scare people with the size of your weapon but without ammunition you can't inflict any damage."

"And you don't think the photo of Monsignor Crowe is ammunition?"

"By itself, no. You have nothing else because Monsignor Crowe's only misstep is seen in that photograph."

"If you truly believe the photo poses no real threat why did you agree to meet with me?"

"Do not mistake my words, Miss Marisol. I would be remiss if I told you I did not care if the photo went public. Such a depiction of Monsignor Crowe would certainly strike a blow against the Church's image and standing. Our enemies, and there are many, would relish in the untold political and social ramifications such a revelation would bring. I asked you here to tonight to try to convince you that Monsignor Crowe is not involved in selling children for sex. Your allegations are simply not true."

"I'm listening. Convince me."

"It is you who needs to convince me. Besides the photo what else do you have?"

"A few days ago five men were found dead in the back of a pickup truck. One of those men etched a phone number into his leather belt just before he was murdered. That phone number belongs to the rectory at St. Basil's."

Cardinal McCrudden rose out of his seat and poured two glasses of water and handed one to me. "Please continue."

"When I went to the rectory I met a pregnant woman,

a Mexican immigrant. She was being paid to have a baby, and the father of that baby is one of the dead men found in the truck. I know there was another pregnant woman, by the name of Itzel, who worked at the rectory. The gardener told me the Monsignor took Itzel away to have her baby. We found Itzel murdered in a cellar of an abandoned church that the Archdiocese used to own."

The Cardinal showed no emotion.

I pressed. "Did you hear what I said?"

The Cardinal calmly continued. "Some years back I was approached, much like your call yesterday, telling me about the same photograph with Monsignor Crowe. At that time the Monsignor hadn't been a parish priest for more than a couple of years. I barely started to build the framework needed to grow the diocese when I received a phone call."

"Who was it?"

The Cardinal ignored my question. "Whoever seeks to keep his life will lose it, but whoever loses his life for My sake, he is the one who will save it."

Impatiently I asked, "What are you talking about?"

I could barely hear the Cardinal mumble. "Luke 9:24."

The Cardinal turned abruptly and held the crucifix out toward me as if I were a vampire whose flesh he needed to burn. "My Lord gave His life, the ultimate sacrifice so that we may one day join Him in Heaven. In His light I have given my life over to the people of this city. I have tried to reach as many souls as I could. I had hoped they would come to know our Lord and open their heart to His glory."

I snapped back. "That is not a justification! I know you sold the church property where Itzel's body was found and a parcel of land in Chávez Ravine to Clay Whitman. I'm guessing you did it to keep Crowe's dirty deed a secret."

Cardinal McCrudden walked over to the window. "I like this room, especially during the day. From this spot I can watch the birds fly in and out of the trees at Pershing Square. So many different species have to live together and they do. There's an order to it."

I couldn't imagine what the Cardinal meant.

"Miss Marisol, what do you think would happen if we erected a birdhouse with food inside and permitted only one bird species to enter?"

"I don't know."

"I will tell you. Disorder would occur. The birds that

could gain entry would grow fat and lazy and become reliant on help. The other birds that couldn't get inside would grow envious and ultimately destroy the birdhouse. Communism is a real threat. Housing projects only breed entitlement and entitlement is the fodder of secularism. Hard work and self-reliance are God-given virtues that we must not turn our back upon."

"Keeping with your model, if every species were allowed to get inside the birdhouse that could solve the problem. In any case, I don't know what birdhouses and communism have to do with Monsignor Crowe. Admit it. You sold the land to Clay Whitman to protect Crowe."

"You have no right to come here and make false accusations. If it had not been for Clay Whitman, communism would have taken deeper root in this city."

"Oh yes. You thought the slated housing project, Elysian Park Heights, was part of a communist plot."

From the side bedroom a voice boomed. "It was."

I turned to see Monsignor Crowe in the doorway. "You've been here the whole time?" It sounded as if I had asked a question, but it was a statement of fact.

Crowe answered. "Yes. I am here at the Cardinal's

request. He asked that I try to convince you I am only guilty of losing sight of my Lord with the woman in the photograph."

"Why are you admitting this now? Why didn't you tell me this when I asked you earlier?"

"I wanted to consult the Cardinal."

"What about Itzel and Graciela? How do you explain them?"

Crowe turned away from me and looked at the Cardinal.

I lost patience. "Don't turn to him. Answer my question. If you're innocent tell me what you know about Itzel and Graciela."

Crowe sat down. "I thought I was helping the women."

"Helping them how? To make money in exchange for a baby?"

Crowe came to his feet. "Yes, the women who came to me were desperate. We, I mean I, didn't see anything wrong with helping them and a family who wanted a baby."

"We? Who's the we?"

Crowe hesitated. "A man named Eduardo Cuevas asked me to help."

"How did you meet him?"

"He attends church at St. Basil's."

"Attends?" I asked.

"Yes, he's usually at the 11:00 service."

"Are you telling me you don't know Eduardo Cuevas is dead?"

"What? When?"

"He was found brutally murdered along with four other men."

"Oh my dear, Lord."

"So you didn't know about Eduardo's murder?"

"I had no idea." Crowe sunk his head into his hands.

"And what about Itzel, Monsignor. You didn't know about her murder either? She was found stabbed. Looks as if it happened shortly after she gave birth."

"I didn't know." Crowe asked with urgency. "What about the baby?"

"There was no sign of a baby."

Crowe pressed again. "Did you talk to anyone from Angel of Mercy? Maybe they know something."

"What's Angel of Mercy?"

"That's where I took Itzel. It's a home for unwed mothers."

The Cardinal who had been quiet now broke into the conversation. "I hope you will drop your course of persecution against Monsignor Crowe. I am prepared to deal with the repercussions if you make the photograph public, but I daresay you won't be."

Had the Cardinal just threatened me? "What do you mean by that?"

"You are young and naïve, Miss Marisol. I am trying to help you before fate catches up with you and I will be helpless to stand in its way. All you have is a photograph, nothing more."

I played my last card. "Do you appreciate the power of science, Cardinal?"

"Now it's my turn. What do you mean, Miss Marisol?"

"Science can be used to reveal the truth. Science can tell us who impregnated the woman found dead in the church cellar."

I turned toward Crowe. "If what you're telling me is correct then science will verify it."

Crowe remained silent, but not the Cardinal. "I am a man of faith, Miss Marisol. That is the only truth I need. I trust you can find your way to the door."

"Yes, of course."

As I closed the door behind me I realized I had been out of my league. My best game had been child's play for the Cardinal.

Chapter 22

GOING DOWN

Unless Olivia's test results could link Crowe to Itzel's baby, I had nothing to tie him to her murder. Was the Cardinal right? Had the Monsignor only been guilty of a sexual indiscretion? A loud ding sounded the elevator's arrival. As I made my descent to the lobby I knew my first order of business; call Armand to see if the DNA results were in. I used the reflection of the elevator's metal pushbutton pad to apply a new coat of lipstick. When I finished, the elevator stopped and the doors opened to the fifth floor.

"Alejandra Marisol, what a surprise."

"Bob, I thought you'd be enjoying a martini and steak by now."

"My plan changed when I met a potential client. How did your meeting with His Eminence turn out?"

"Not as productive as I had hoped."

"Sorry to hear that."

As Bob Dennon moved into the carriage his foot appeared to get caught in the grate of the doorway.

"Damn, my heel is stuck."

I bent down to try and help. Bob reacted to my gesture. He quickly placed his hand over my face and tightly pressed a damp cloth against my mouth and nose. I tried to fight. The fumes from a strong solvent reached their way up my nasal passages and left me defenseless as he dragged me out of the elevator and into a room across the hall. I heard the door close and then everything went black.

§§§§§§§

My eyes strained to focus. What had just happened? I instinctively moved to stand, but couldn't. My arms and legs were tightly bound against a wooden chair. Seconds passed before it came back to me. Bob Dennon had knocked me out with some sort of chemical, chloroform, I'd guess. How Dennon fit into the puzzle I didn't know and it really didn't matter. I had to figure out a way to get free and be quick about it.

I tried to think clearly, but the throbbing pain in my head and the taped cloth stuffed in my mouth didn't help. I struggled to breathe and soon found myself in a state of terror. Hope was slipping away. Through my tears, a vision of my mom appeared. She kept her distance and didn't say a word, but I could see her love for me in her eyes. It was a familiar expression, one I remembered from my childhood. Today, as in the past, it filled me with strength and freed me from self-doubt. As quickly as she appeared she was gone and I didn't hesitate to use the courage she brought me. I rocked the chair from side to side using the momentum to move to a window covered by a heavy drape. When I made it, I rocked one more time knocking the chair into the glass. The drape, as I had hoped, kept the glass from slicing into my flesh as it splintered.

Now that I had broken the window what could I do? The window stood too high to try and use the shards to cut away the ropes binding my arms and hands. My best option was to use a hanging shard to cut away the tape across my mouth. I tipped my chair, relying on the sill to hold me at a 30 degree angle as I used a pointed edge of glass to cut through the tape. Within a few seconds I was able to spit out the gag, but my upper lip had paid the price. I felt the taste of warm blood running into my mouth as I heard a key enter the lock. I pushed my head through the window hoping to catch sight of a passerby from five floors above the ground, but no luck. Before Bob Dennon pulled me away from the window I lapped up a broken shard of glass.

Dennon grabbed my chair and dragged it to the middle of the room. "Ashworth was right. You have a lot of fight."

I didn't respond. I couldn't. I had to focus on not swallowing the sharp object resting on my tongue.

"Nothing to say. No questions to ask?"

I gave him a blank stare.

"That's okay, Alejandra. I'll look forward to hearing your sweet moan when I start to peel the first bit of skin away from the fascia. That's usually when it starts: the begging. And don't think anyone will hear you. I made sure to reserve the rooms next door and across the hall. We'll have lots of privacy, you and me.

Dennon rolled out sheets of plastic onto the floor and discussed his plan. "Don't want to leave a mess behind. Sometimes it doesn't matter, but tonight it does. Ashworth was good about being clean, like me, when he needed to. You know, I taught him everything. He took to it right away too. He really loved to inflict pain. I felt I knew that about him the first day I met him. He was with Gary Bell. They showed up at a flophouse trying to arrest some of my whores."

Dennon saw the uncertain look in my eyes.

"I paid off the manager so I could use the top floor as a profitable whorehouse. Right away I sensed Ashworth's and Bell's greed, so all I had to do was offer them a better deal than what LAPD paid. Cops are so easy to manipulate. I showed them a storage closet with a bird's eye view of one of the rooms. The pictures they took of clients who needed to keep their indiscretions secret brought them quite a large chunk of cash. In exchange they left my little enterprise alone. Soon enough they got used to the money and that's when I owned them. The rest is history. They worked to help me build a good business. Make children to sell. It's ingenious. But I didn't do it for the money. I did it for the pleasure." Dennon walked closer toward me. "You've been tracking me and getting closer. You made me kill Gary Bell and those five men. Now you have to go. It could have been different. All you had to do was let Ashworth take the blame for the Belvedere Park murders. If it were up to me, Crowe and McCrudden would be joining you; but they're still invaluable, at least my father thinks so."

Dennon noticed my eyes widen. "You see the resemblance don't you? My father doesn't have my good looks, but I have his blood running through me."

Yes, now I saw it. Bob Dennon was Clay Whitman's son. Gary Bell knew the familial tie and was rightfully afraid.

"When I was thirteen, Father, changed my name and sent me away. He had no other choice. He wasn't about to lose his only son even though I had murdered his daughter, my sister, Roberta. Everyone thought I had died in a fire alongside Roberta, but as you can see I am far from dead. I staged my death so I could get rid of her. I hated her and she had to go. I planned her death for over a year. I pretended to make friends with a boy from a different neighborhood. One day I invited him to play with us at the house. Told him he couldn't tell anyone he was coming over, and if he could pull it off, I'd give him a hundred dollar bill. What a gullible moron; he didn't deserve to live. I locked him in the basement with my sister and set the house on fire."

I didn't know who was more depraved, Bob Dennon or John Ashworth.

"I brought us a nice bottle of champagne for the occasion. Let me pop this open and make a toast before I have to put the gag back in that bleeding mouth of yours."

Dennon walked over to the table to uncork the bottle and pour the champagne and then walked back to me. "I'll free your hands so we can properly toast."

I couldn't believe what I heard. It was my only shot to take him down and I couldn't fail.

Dennon pulled a knife from his pocket and cut through the ropes binding my arms and hands to the chair.

He then handed me a Dixie cup filled with champagne. "I can't risk giving you a glass, but I think you'll still find the taste exquisite even with a paper cup. It's *Perrier-Jouët*, one of the finest champagnes."

Dennon brought his glass up to the light. "I never get bored looking at these bubbles. They're endless."

Dennon stared at his glass for what seemed like an eternity. When he finished he turned his sight back on me and smiled. "You know, I let my guard down with Itzel and got her pregnant. I let her beauty cloud my judgment. Poor thing, she never saw it coming. I think she believed we would be a family."

Dennon lifted his glass in the air. "What shall we toast to?"

I stared in his direction and intentionally avoided his eyes. I dismissed him and he responded with rage.

"Damn you, Alejandra. You can't play along. It would make things a lot easier."

Dennon paused to compose himself. "That's okay. We will toast to me and the business of making and selling children. There really is nothing more profitable when you figure in the minimal investment that's required. Now drink. Drink to me."

I needed to get Dennon closer to me. I brought the cup up to my mouth. I wet my finger in the champagne and ran it across my lips.

"Damn, you're sexy. It's too bad I have to kill you. But until then..."

Dennon pushed into me and pressed his lips over mine. I couldn't give into my disgust. I focused and waited for him to open his mouth. As soon as I felt his lips part I exhaled with all of my force and blew the shard of glass into his throat. Dennon quickly backed away and I saw his eyes roll into his head. From what I could I see I had made the perfect pitch.

Dennon grabbed at his throat and tried to cough up

the shard, but it wouldn't budge. He struggled to breath and then collapsed to the floor. As he moaned and gasped for air his outstretched arm and clenched fist pleaded for help. He appealed to the wrong person. I had no empathy in my soul for this man.

By the time hotel security arrived, Dennon had started to turn blue. He was barely alive and mentally, I was right there with him.

Chapter 23

RECKONING

Several days had passed before Olivia confirmed, using a strand of Dennon's hair and the umbilical cord still attached to the placenta, that Dennon fathered Itzel's missing baby. Olivia's analysis also showed that samples retrieved from the handle of the knife used to kill Itzel matched Dennon's DNA. Even though the results had cleared Crowe, I wasn't convinced he and the Cardinal were free of wrongdoing, but I had nowhere to turn. As for the Cardinal's role, he refused to admit he had been blackmailed into transferring ownership of Archdiocese property to Clay Whitman, and I had no way to determine otherwise. Not even Gary Bell could help me. Gary's death remained undetermined. No evidence at the crime scene could definitively prove he had been murdered or that Bob Dennon was involved. As for Crowe, employees at Angel of Mercy told me the Monsignor dropped off pregnant women before they were ready to give birth. When the women went into labor Dr. Stevens, a physician who offered free medical services to indigent pregnant women, stepped in to help. Angel of Mercy staff identified Bob Dennon as the man who called himself Dr. Stevens and they never questioned the doctor's motives. Dr. Stevens presented his credentials and, given their limited resources, they were happy for the support. By their estimate Dr. Stevens had been called to deliver more than twenty babies from women whom Crowe had dropped off. When I asked about the fate of the mothers and their babies, they had no information to offer.

When news of Dennon's death became public, Ashworth's LAPD accomplices started to talk. Their knowledge of Dennon's enterprise was limited and they had no evidence linking Dennon to any of the crimes. Nevertheless they feared for their lives, believing if they talked to the police Dennon would have found a way to kill them, brutally, like the five murdered men found in the truck bed. They pointed to Ashworth's suicide as proof it was better to kill yourself than give Dennon the pleasure. With the promise of a plea deal, the accomplices told investigators that the plan depended on coaxing Mexican immigrant women into becoming surrogate mothers for a nominal fee. After the children were born the unwitting mothers were murdered and the babies sold to the highest bidder. The accomplices led police back to Ashworth's house where sale transaction records and baby photos were found taped behind a painting of a boat tied alongside a riverbank; the same one I had seen hanging on the wall. Although investigators were not able to determine the whereabouts of all the children, three were rescued.

DNA testing determined that none of the rescued children had been born to Itzel and I wasn't surprised. The more I thought about it the more I couldn't reconcile Dennon selling his own flesh and blood, no matter how sadistic and evil he was. I had a hunch. I called on Captain Allen to help me confirm my suspicion. I knew he would appreciate any chance to make up for his late arrival to the Biltmore Hotel.

§§§§§§§

The gates leading up to the Whitman estate off of Mulholland Drive were closed and locked when we arrived, but an intercom hung on a post off to the side. Captain Allen exited the car and pushed the button. A voice on the other end answered. "Whitman residence."

"Hello. I'm Captain Allen from LAPD. I'd like to speak to Mr. Clay Whitman."

We heard no response to Captain Allen's request. We waited not knowing what to think, but then after a couple of minutes the gates opened. As we slowly drove up the driveway we snaked through lush landscaped grounds filled with Date Palms and Elephant Ears before reaching the expansive two-story mansion. We didn't need to knock on the door. Clay Whitman waited for us outside.

"Hello, Mr. Whitman." I announced.

"Miss Marisol, I had a feeling Captain Allen wasn't traveling alone. Still I didn't think you'd have the nerve to show your face here."

"Why is that, Mr. Whitman? Because in order to save myself I had to kill your son?"

Clay Whitman turned his back toward me and addressed Captain Allen. "I didn't have to let you onto my property, but I did. So what is it you want?"

"Honestly Mr. Whitman, I'm here in an unofficial capacity. My role is to accompany Miss Marisol and make sure she stays safe."

"Well, if that's what's going on you can get back into your car and get the hell off my property."

I interjected, "Mr. Whitman, I have a quick question."

Clay Whitman raised his voice. "Did you not hear me? I said get the hell out of here. And unless you have a warrant, don't you ever come back."

I turned to leave and then stopped when I heard a baby's cry coming from a second floor window. Whitman didn't hesitate to respond. "That baby doesn't concern you."

"But I am concerned, Mr. Whitman. Have you heard of DNA fingerprinting? It's a technique that will prove the baby belongs to your son, Bob Dennon. Or should we call him by his birth name, Robert Whitman?"

"Do you take me for a stupid man?"

"Of course not."

"Good, because I'm way ahead of you. I already know about this so-called DNA evidence that the Coroner submitted to the District Attorney's office. The DA is a friend of mine and I know what's been submitted is not going to be admissible should anyone try to involve me or drag my son, known to have died years ago in a house fire, through the mud. DNA testing has no precedence, plain and simple."

"But you know he never died in that fire. That makes you an accessory."

"That's not how the law will see it. You have nothing. What was it you told me the other day? Men like me won't see it coming and won't be prepared when people like you make a move to take us down. I've been prepared for people like you my whole life. I've seen you coming, Miss Marisol, way before the thought to come after me ever entered your mind." Clay Whitman stepped closer. "This world cannot run without men like me. The system would crumble. You depend on us to breathe and eat. Yes, Miss Marisol, without men like me you don't get to exist."

I held my ground. "You've covered up your son's perversions for a long time. He must have sickened you. He killed your daughter. How do you live with yourself?"

Clay Whitman was done. "You don't understand English. Leave right now before I have you arrested for trespassing and harassment."

I continued. "Don't you give a damn about the children sold by your son? You have a grandchild upstairs; you must feel something."

Whitman turned to address Captain Allen. "If you

don't leave and take this woman with you, I'll make sure your career is finished."

Captain Allen got back in the car and motioned for me to do the same. I sunk into the seat. Whitman had managed to wrestle my spirit free and it was now lying in a puddle at his feet. This battle had been lost. Whitman's power and connections made it so.

We drove away from the property and I didn't know how I'd be able to move forward. Bob Dennon had inflicted unimaginable horror and his death offered no consolation.

From the banked curves of Mulholland Drive I looked down onto a sprawling city with no end in sight. Somewhere on a palm tree lined street there was a child being abused to service someone's pleasure. I had to tolerate this fact; the price for living in this world. But tolerance is very different from acceptance and I wasn't about to accept the brutal pain inflicted by humans. The water of life remains in the dead, but it was also inside of me, hydrating and fortifying my resolve.

"Can you pull over?"

Captain Allen turned into an overlook, a large patch of dirt off the road. I got out of the car and stood to see my city. I reached for my lipstick and removed the cap. I rolled the tube across my mouth and then pressed my lips together to even out the color. Instantly I felt my spirit make its way back home to me. For now Clay Whitman was out of reach, but there were more like him who used their wealth to hide their offenses in the dark. I knew it would be a struggle, but without patience I'd be lost. Like my grandmother, *Nana*, told me, "*La paciencia es como el sol, sin él que no sé este del oeste.*" Patience is like the sun, without it you don't know east from west. I had my sense of direction in check and it was leading me into the shadows. It was there I had to go to shine the light.

Made in the USA
San Bernardino, CA
24 January 2017